It's another Quality Book from CGP

This book is for anyone doing GCSE Single Science.

First we take all the _really important stuff_
you need to pass GCSE Single Science
— and we stick it in a book.

Then we have a real good stab at trying
to make it funny — so you'll _actually use it_.
Simple as that.

Higher | This book is suitable for both Higher and Foundation Tier candidates.
The material which is required only for Higher Tier is clearly indicated in blue boxes like this.
In addition, the Higher Tier questions in the Revision Summaries are printed in blue. | **Higher**

What CGP is all about

Our sole aim here at CGP is to produce the highest quality
books — carefully written, immaculately presented and
dangerously close to being funny.

Then we work our socks off to get them out to you
— at the cheapest possible prices.

Published by Coordination Group Publications Ltd.

Contributors: Charley Darbishire
                  Simon Little
                  Andy Park
                  Glenn Rogers
                  Claire Thompson

Based on original material by Richard Parsons

ISBN: 1-84146-210-1
Groovy website: www.cgpbooks.co.uk

Printed by Elanders Hindson, Newcastle upon Tyne.
Jolly bits of clipart from CorelDRAW

With thanks to Glenn Rogers for the proofreading

1102

Cells, Tissues and Organ Systems

Animal Cells have Four Main Features

You need to be able to draw cells with these <u>details</u>.

1) <u>Nucleus</u>
contains genetic material that controls what the cell <u>does</u>.

2) <u>Cytoplasm</u>
contains enzymes that speed up biological reactions.

3) <u>Cell membrane</u>
holds the cell together and controls what goes <u>in</u> and <u>out</u>.

4) <u>Mitochondria</u>
turn glucose and oxygen into <u>energy</u>.

Cells, Tissues, Organs and Organ Systems

They like asking this in Exams, so learn the sequence:

> A group of <u>SIMILAR CELLS</u> is called a <u>TISSUE</u>.
> A group of <u>DIFFERENT TISSUES</u> form an <u>ORGAN</u>.
> A <u>GROUP OF ORGANS</u> working together form an <u>ORGAN SYSTEM</u>,
> or even <u>A WHOLE ORGANISM</u>.

Cells are Specialised for their Function

Most cells are <u>specialised</u> for a specific job, and in the Exam you'll probably have to explain why the cell they've shown you is so good at its job. It's a lot easier if you've <u>already learnt them</u>!

1) Red blood cells are Designed to Carry Oxygen

1) They're <u>small</u> and <u>doughnut</u> shaped to give a big surface area for oxygen absorption.
2) They contain <u>haemoglobin</u> which carries oxygen.
3) They're <u>flexible</u> to allow smooth passage through the <u>capillaries</u>.
4) They're unusual because they don't need a <u>nucleus</u>.

2) White blood cells are made to Fight Disease

White blood cells have a <u>flexible shape</u>.
This allows them to engulf <u>disease organisms</u>.

3) Sperm and Egg cells are specialised for Reproduction

1) The <u>egg</u> cell has huge food reserves to provide nutrition for the developing embryo.
2) When a <u>sperm</u> fuses with the egg, the egg's <u>membrane</u> instantly changes to prevent any more sperm getting in.
3) A long tail gives the sperm the <u>mobility</u> needed for its long journey to find the egg.
4) The sperm also has a <u>short life-span</u> so only the fittest survive the race to the egg.

Size of sperm in relation to the egg

Sperm

I'd cell my soul to get out of learning this...

If you're doing the <u>OCR A</u> syllabus you have to learn that living things show these 7 life processes:

M — Movement ...... *being able to <u>move</u> parts of the body*
R — Reproduction ... *producing <u>offspring</u>*
S — Sensitivity .... *<u>responding</u> to the outside world*
N — Nutrition ....*getting <u>food</u> in where it's needed*
E — Excretion ....*<u>getting rid</u> of waste products*
R — Respiration ...... *turning <u>food</u> into <u>energy</u>*
G — Growth ....*getting to <u>adult size</u>*

The Digestive System

You'll definitely get a question on this in your Exam so take your time and learn this very important diagram in all its infinite glory. And that includes the words too:

Ten Bits of Your Grisly Digestive System to Learn:

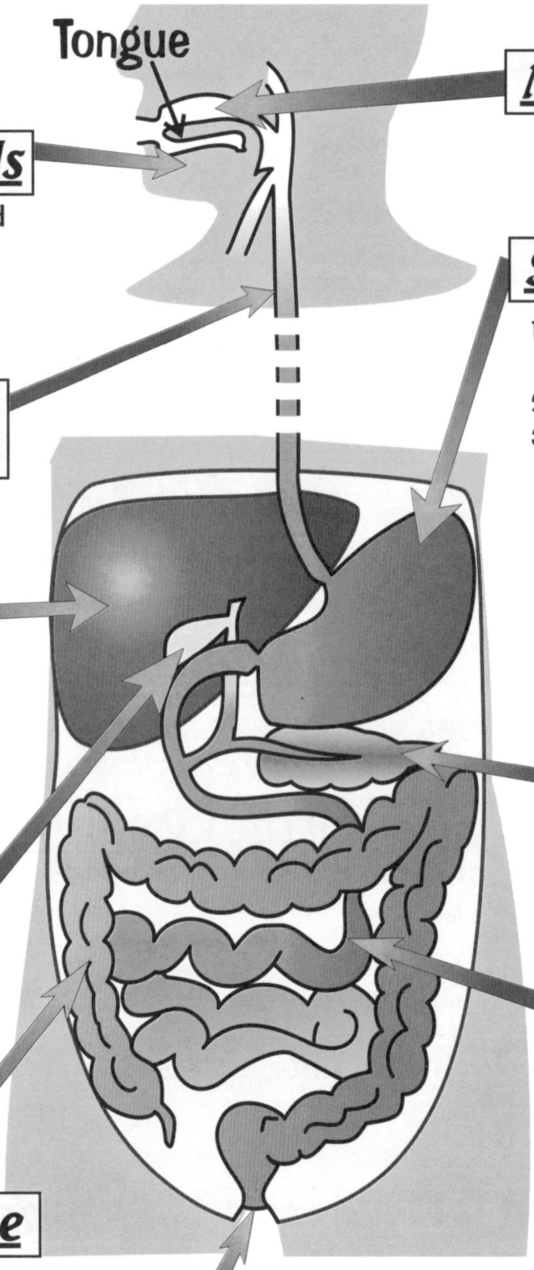

Tongue

Mouth
Chews food up into easy-to-swallow balls.

Salivary Glands
Produce an enzyme called amylase to start the breakdown of starch.

Stomach
1) It pummels the food with its muscular walls.
2) It produces protease enzymes.
3) It produces hydrochloric acid for two reasons:
  a) To kill bacteria
  b) To give the right pH for the protease enzyme to work (pH2 — acidic).

Oesophagus
(Your gullet)
The food chute from the mouth to the stomach.

Liver
Where bile is produced. Bile emulsifies fats and neutralises stomach acid (to make conditions right for the enzymes in the small intestine).

Pancreas
Produces the lot: amylase, lipase and the protease, enzymes.

Gall bladder
Where bile is stored, before it's injected into the intestine.

Small intestine
1) Produces the protease, amylase and lipase enzymes.
2) This is also where the "food" is absorbed into the blood.
3) It's long and folded to increase surface area. Tiny finger-like things called villi cover the inner surface to increase the surface area even more.

Large intestine
Where excess water is absorbed from the food.

Anus
Where the faeces (made mostly of indigestible food) bid you a fond farewell.

Have you learned the Whole Diagram?
The one thing they won't ask you to do in the Exam is draw the whole thing out yourself. BUT they will ask you about any part of it, e.g. "What is the position of the liver?", or "What does the pancreas produce?", or "What is the function of bile?" So in the end you have to learn the whole thing anyway. And that means being able to cover the page and draw it out, words and all. If you can't draw it all out from memory — then you haven't learnt it. Simple as that.

The Digestive System

All the Way Along there's Muscular and Glandular Tissue

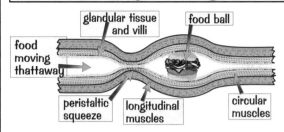

food moving thattaway

glandular tissue and villi

food ball

peristaltic squeeze

longitudinal muscles

circular muscles

There's <u>muscular</u> tissue all the way down the digestive system. Its job is to <u>squeeze</u> the food along. This squeezing action is called <u>peristalsis</u>.

The inside layer is <u>glandular</u> tissue which produces <u>enzymes</u>, as well as a protective <u>mucus</u>.

The Villi Provide a Really Really Big Surface Area

The inside of the <u>small intestine</u> is covered in millions and millions of these tiny little projections called <u>villi</u>.

They increase the surface area in a big way so that digested food is <u>absorbed</u> much more quickly into the <u>blood</u>. Notice they have
1) a <u>single</u> layer of cells,
2) a very good <u>blood supply</u> to assist <u>quick absorption</u>.

a villus

another villus

network of capillaries

circular muscle

longitudinal muscle

gland cells

Enzymes break down Big Molecules into Small Ones

1) <u>Starch</u>, <u>proteins</u> and <u>fats</u> are <u>big</u> molecules which can't pass through cell walls into the blood.
2) <u>Sugars</u>, <u>amino acids</u> and <u>fatty acids/glycerol</u> are <u>much smaller</u> molecules which can pass easily into the blood.
3) <u>Enzymes</u> act as <u>catalysts</u> to break down the <u>big molecules</u> into the <u>smaller ones</u>.

1) Amylase Converts Starch into Simple Sugars

<u>Amylase</u> is produced in <u>three</u> places:
1) <u>The Salivary glands</u>
2) <u>The Pancreas</u>
3) <u>The small intestine</u>

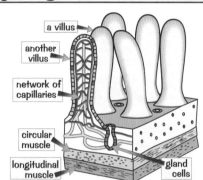

Starch

Amylase enzymes

Glucose
and other simple sugars, e.g. maltose

2) Proteases Convert Proteins into Amino Acids

Proteases are produced in <u>three</u> places: 1) <u>The stomach</u> (where it's called <u>pepsin</u>), 2) <u>The pancreas</u>, 3) The <u>small intestine</u>.

Proteins

Protease enzymes

Amino acids

3) Lipases Convert Fats into Fatty Acids and Glycerol

Lipases are produced in <u>two</u> places:
1) <u>The pancreas</u>
2) <u>The small intestine</u>

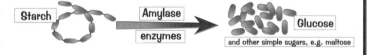

Fat

Lipase enzymes

Fatty acids & glycerol

4) Bile Neutralises the Stomach Acid and Emulsifies Fats

1) It's <u>alkaline</u> to <u>neutralise</u> the acid from the stomach to make conditions right for the enzymes in the small intestine to work.
2) It <u>emulsifies fats</u>. In other words it breaks the fat into <u>tiny droplets</u>. This gives a much <u>bigger surface area</u> of fat for the enzyme lipase to work on. Nothing too tricky there.

Higher

Higher

Diffusion of "Food" Molecules

The Big Food Molecules Must First be Broken Down

After you've chewed your food up and your stomach's had its turn at munching it up still further, it's still made up of <u>quite big molecules</u>, namely: <u>Starch</u>, <u>Proteins</u> and <u>Fats</u>.

These are still <u>too big</u> to diffuse into the blood, and so they are broken down in the small intestine into <u>smaller</u> molecules: <u>glucose</u>, <u>amino acids</u>, <u>fatty acids</u> and <u>glycerol</u>.

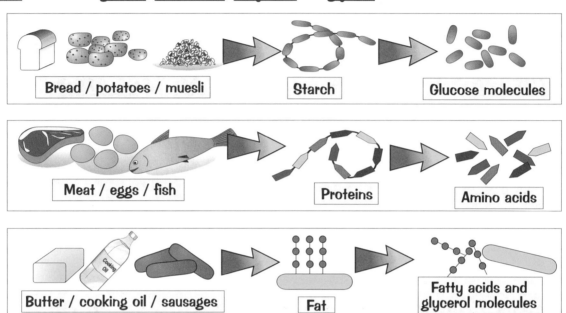

Bread / potatoes / muesli → Starch → Glucose molecules

Meat / eggs / fish → Proteins → Amino acids

Butter / cooking oil / sausages → Fat → Fatty acids and glycerol molecules

The Small Molecules Can Then Diffuse into the Blood

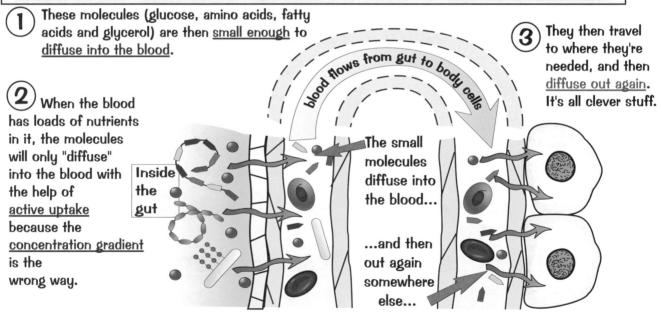

(1) These molecules (glucose, amino acids, fatty acids and glycerol) are then <u>small enough</u> to <u>diffuse into the blood</u>.

(2) When the blood has loads of nutrients in it, the molecules will only "diffuse" into the blood with the help of <u>active uptake</u> because the <u>concentration gradient</u> is the wrong way.

blood flows from gut to body cells

(3) They then travel to where they're needed, and then <u>diffuse out again</u>. It's all clever stuff.

Inside the gut

The small molecules diffuse into the blood...

...and then out again somewhere else...

Let's see what you've LEARNED, shall we...

Practise answering these three questions until you can do them all <u>without looking at the page</u>.
If you can't, then it means just one thing — you haven't learnt it. (Pretty obviously)

1) Name the three big molecules that <u>won't</u> diffuse into the blood.
2) Name the four small molecules that <u>will</u> diffuse into the blood.

Blood

Red Blood Cells

1) Their job is to carry oxygen to all the cells in the body.

Higher

2) They have a flying doughnut shape to give maximum surface area for absorbing oxygen.
3) They contain haemoglobin, which contains a lot of iron, and which when combined with oxygen is very red.
4) In the lungs, haemoglobin absorbs oxygen to become oxyhaemoglobin. In body tissues the reverse happens to release oxygen to the cells.
5) Red blood cells have no need for a nucleus, so they don't have one, making more room for haemoglobin.

White Blood Cells

1) Their main role is defence against disease.
2) They have a big nucleus.
3) They gobble up unwelcome micro-organisms.
4) They produce antibodies to fight bacteria.
5) They produce antitoxins to neutralise the toxins produced by bacteria.

Plasma

This is a pale straw-coloured liquid which carries just about everything:

1) Red and white blood cells and platelets.
2) Nutrients like glucose and amino acids.
3) Carbon dioxide.
4) Urea.
5) Hormones.
6) Antibodies and antitoxins produced by the white blood cells.

Platelets

1) These are small fragments of cells.
2) They have no nucleus.
3) They help the blood to clot at a wound. This stops all your blood pouring out and stops micro organisms getting in.
(So basically they just float about waiting for accidents to happen!)

More Blood, Sweat and Tears...

Do the same as usual — learn the facts until you can write them down from memory.

Just in case you think all this formal learning is a waste of time, how do you think you'd get on with these typical Exam questions if you didn't learn it all first?

Three typical Exam questions:
1) What is the function of blood plasma? (4 marks)
2) What do white blood cells do? (3 marks)
3) What is the function of haemoglobin? (4 marks)

The Nervous System

Sense Organs and Receptors

The five sense organs are:
Eyes ears nose tongue skin

These five different sense organs all contain different receptors.

Receptors are groups of cells which are sensitive to a stimulus such as light or heat, etc.

Sense organs and Receptors
Don't get them mixed up:

The eye is a sense organ — it contains light receptors (rods and cones).
The ear is a sense organ — it contains sound-receptors.

Receptors are cells that turn energy (e.g. light energy) into electrical impulses.

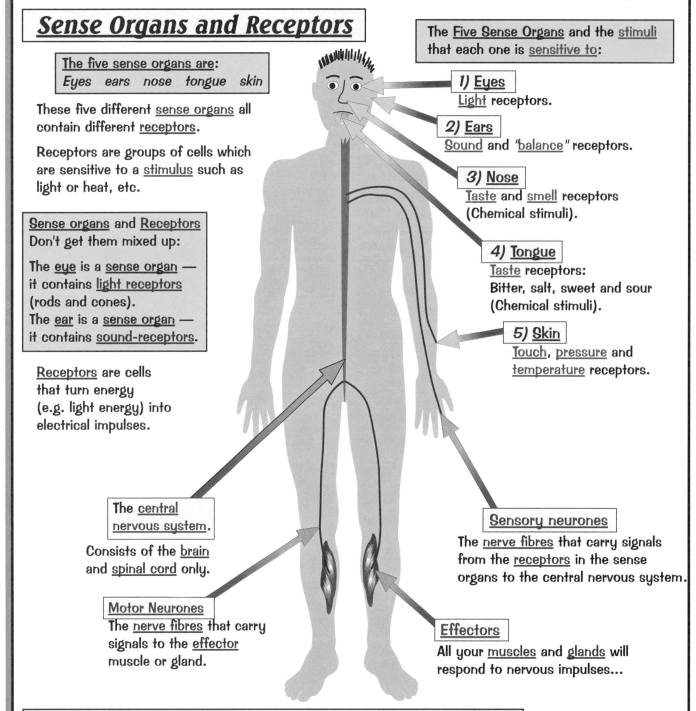

The Five Sense Organs and the stimuli that each one is sensitive to:

1) Eyes
Light receptors.

2) Ears
Sound and "balance" receptors.

3) Nose
Taste and smell receptors (Chemical stimuli).

4) Tongue
Taste receptors:
Bitter, salt, sweet and sour (Chemical stimuli).

5) Skin
Touch, pressure and temperature receptors.

The central nervous system.
Consists of the brain and spinal cord only.

Motor Neurones
The nerve fibres that carry signals to the effector muscle or gland.

Sensory neurones
The nerve fibres that carry signals from the receptors in the sense organs to the central nervous system.

Effectors
All your muscles and glands will respond to nervous impulses...

The Central Nervous System and Effectors

1) The central nervous system is where all the sensory information is sent and where reflexes and actions are coordinated. It consists of the brain and spinal cord only.
2) Neurones (nerve cells) transmit electrical impulses very quickly around the body.
3) The effectors are muscles and glands which respond to the various stimuli according to the instructions sent from the central nervous system.

This stuff is easy — I mean it's all just common senses...

There's quite a few names to learn here (as ever!).
But there's no drivel. It's all worth marks in the Exam, so learn it all.
Practise until you can cover the page and scribble down all the details from memory.

The Nervous System

The Three Types of Neurone are All Much The Same

The THREE TYPES of NEURONE are:

(They're all *pretty much the same*, they're just *connected to different things*, that's all.)

1) *SENSORY neurone*
2) *MOTOR neurone*
3) *RELAY neurone* (or *CONNECTOR neurone*).

A Typical Neurone: — *Learn the names* of all the bits:

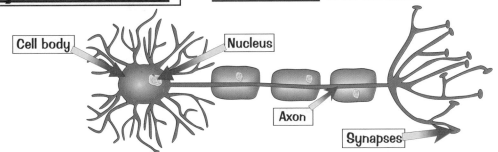

Cell body

Nucleus

Axon

Synapses

Synapses Use Chemicals

A Synapse

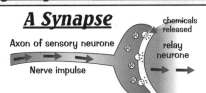

chemicals released

relay neurone

Axon of sensory neurone

Nerve impulse

1) The connection between two neurones is called a synapse.
2) The nerve signal is transferred by chemicals which diffuse across the gap.
3) These chemicals then set off a new electrical signal in the next neurone.

The Reflex Arc Allows Very Quick Responses

A Typical Reflex Arc

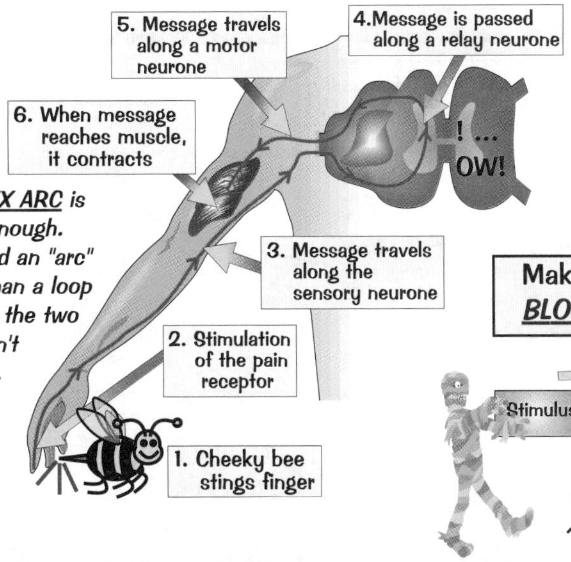

5. Message travels along a motor neurone

4. Message is passed along a relay neurone

6. When message reaches muscle, it contracts

! ... OW!

A *REFLEX ARC* is simple enough. It's called an "arc" rather than a loop because the two ends don't connect.

3. Message travels along the sensory neurone

2. Stimulation of the pain receptor

1. Cheeky bee stings finger

1) The nervous system allows very quick responses because it uses electrical impulses.
2) Reflex actions are automatic (i.e. done without thinking) so they are even quicker.
3) Reflex actions save your body from injury, e.g. pulling your hand off a hot object for you.
4) A muscle responds by contracting, a gland responds by secreting.

Make sure you also learn the *BLOCK DIAGRAM* of a Reflex Arc:

Stimulus | Receptor | Sensory neurone | Relay neurone | Motor neurone | Effector | Response

Receptors: cones and rods

Don't get all twitchy — just learn it...

Another jolly page to learn, but it's all good clean fun. Once again, everything on this page is important information that you definitely need to know for the Exams. Use the diagrams to help you remember the important details. Then cover the page and scribble it all down.

Higher Higher Higher Higher Higher Higher

The Eye

Learn The Eye with all its labels:

1) The <u>pupil</u> is the <u>hole</u> in the middle of the iris, which the light goes through.
2) The eye is filled with a <u>clear liquid</u> which <u>supports</u> the spherical shape of the eye.
3) The <u>retina</u> is the <u>light sensitive</u> part and is covered in <u>rods</u> and <u>cones</u> which detect light.
4) <u>Rods</u> are more sensitive in <u>dim light</u> but only sense in <u>black and white</u>.
5) <u>Cones</u> are sensitive to <u>colours</u> but are not so good in dim light.
6) The <u>fovea</u> is a spot with loads of tightly packed cones which gives a really sharp image when you look straight at something.

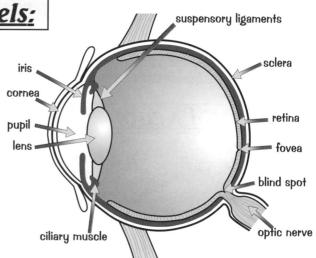

Adjusting for Light and Dark — the IRIS

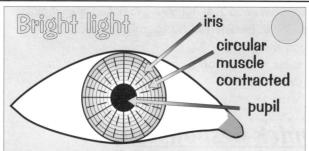

1) The circular muscles <u>contract</u>.
2) The iris <u>closes up</u>, the pupil gets <u>smaller</u>.
3) <u>Less</u> light gets into the eye.

1) The radial muscles <u>contract</u>.
2) The iris <u>opens out</u>, the pupil gets <u>bigger</u>.
3) This lets <u>more light</u> into the eye.

Focusing on Near and Distant Objects

Higher

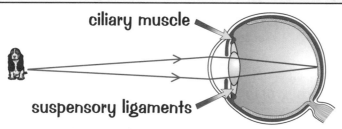

Higher

<u>To look at distant objects:</u>
1) The <u>ciliary muscles relax</u>, which allows the <u>suspensory ligaments</u> to <u>pull tight</u>.
2) This makes the lens go <u>thin</u>.

<u>To look at near objects:</u>
1) The <u>ciliary muscles contract</u> which <u>slackens</u> the <u>suspensory ligaments</u>.
2) The lens becomes <u>fat</u>.

Let's see what you've learned then...

This is a pretty straightforward page of information. You need to make sure you know all the diagrams with all labels and also the numbered points for each.
Practise until you can <u>scribble</u> the whole lot down <u>from memory</u>.

Hormones

Hormones are Chemical Messengers sent in the Blood

1) Hormones are chemicals released directly into the blood.
2) They are carried in the blood to other parts of the body.
3) They are produced in various glands (endocrine glands) as shown on the diagram.
4) They travel all over the body but only affect particular cells in particular places.
5) They travel at "the speed of blood".
6) They have long-lasting effects.
7) They control things that need constant adjustment.

learn this definition:

Hormones ...
are chemical messengers
which travel in the blood
to activate target cells.

The Pituitary Gland
This produces many important hormones: LH, FSH and ADH.
These tend to control other glands, as a rule.

Adrenal Gland
Produces adrenaline which prepares the body with the well known fight or flight reaction:
Increased blood sugar, heart rate, breathing rate, and diversion of blood from skin to muscles.

Pancreas
Produces insulin for the control of blood sugar (If you're doing AQA it also produces glucagon).

Kidney

Ovaries — females only
Produce oestrogen which promotes all female secondary sexual characteristics during puberty:
1) Extra hair in places.
2) Changes in body proportions.
3) Egg production.

Testes — males only
Produce testosterone which promotes all male secondary sexual characteristics at puberty:
1) Extra hair in places.
2) Changes in body proportions.
3) Sperm production.

Hormones and Nerves do Similar Jobs, but there are Important Differences

Nerves:
1) Very fast message.
2) Act for a very short time.
3) Act on a very precise area.
4) Immediate reaction.

Hormones:
1) Slower message.
2) Act for a long time.
3) Act in a more general way.
4) Longer-term reaction.

Hormones — Easy peasy...

Well let's face it, there's not much to learn here is there? The diagram and all its labels are easy enough, and so's the comparison of nerves and hormones. The definition of hormones is worth learning word for word. The seven points at the top of the page are best done with the good old mini-essay" method. Learn it, cover the page and scribble. Then try again. And smile of course.

The Menstrual Cycle

1) The *monthly* release of an *egg* from a woman's *ovaries* and the build up and break down of a protective lining in the *womb* is called the *menstrual cycle*.

2) *Hormones* released by the *pituitary gland* (P. 9) and the *ovaries* control the different stages of the menstrual cycle.

The Menstrual Cycle has Four Stages

STAGE 1 *Day 1 is when the bleeding starts*. The uterus lining breaks down for about four days.

STAGE 2 *The lining of the womb builds up again*, from day 4 to day 14, into a thick spongy layer of blood vessels ready to receive a fertilised egg.

STAGE 3 *An egg is developed and then released* from the ovary at day 14.

STAGE 4 *The wall is maintained* for about 14 days, until day 28. If no fertilised egg has landed on the uterus wall by day 28, the lining breaks down again and the cycle starts over.

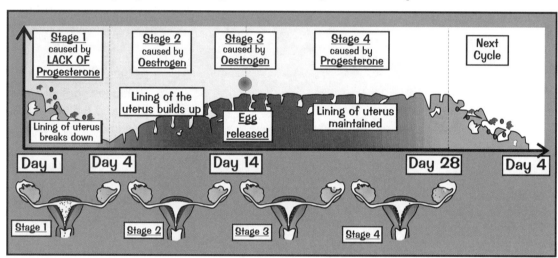

There are Three Main Hormones involved

1) *FSH (Follicle Stimulating Hormone) — Used to Stimulate Egg Production in Fertility Treatment:*

1) Produced by the *pituitary gland*.
2) Causes an *egg to develop in one of the ovaries*.
3) Stimulates the *ovaries to produce oestrogen*.

1) *FSH* can be taken by women (who have low levels of FSH) to stimulate *egg production* in their *ovaries*.
2) It stimulates the *ovaries* to produce *oestrogen* which in turn stimulates the *release of an egg*.

2) *OESTROGEN — Used to Stop Egg Production in "The PILL":*

1) Produced in the *ovaries*.
2) Causes *pituitary* to produce *LH*.
3) *Inhibits* the further release of *FSH*.

1) "THE PILL" is an oral contraceptive containing oestrogen.
2) It's kind of strange but even though oestrogen stimulates the release of eggs, if oestrogen is taken every day to keep the level of it permanently high, it inhibits the production of FSH and after a while egg production stops and stays stopped.
3) Once you stop taking it, things gradually return to normal.

3) *LH (Luteinising Hormone):*

1) Produced by the *pituitary gland*.
2) Stimulates the *release of an egg* at roughly the middle of the menstrual cycle.

Female or otherwise, you've still gotta learn it...

This is the relatively simple stuff on the menstrual cycle and it's definitely well worth learning. Make sure you know what the hormones do and where they are produced, and also how hormones are used to control fertility. *Learn and enjoy.*

Homeostasis

Homeostasis is a fancy word.

DON'T GET IT CONFUSED WITH HORMONES COZ THEY ARE COMPLETELY DIFFERENT THINGS... OK!

Homeostasis covers all the functions of your body which try to maintain a "constant internal environment".

Learn the definition:

HOMEOSTASIS — the maintenance of a CONSTANT INTERNAL ENVIRONMENT

There are six different bodily levels that need to be controlled:

1) REMOVAL OF CO_2
2) REMOVAL OF Urea
} These two are wastes. They're constantly produced in the body and you just need to get rid of them.

3) Ion content
4) Water content
5) Sugar content
6) Temperature
} These four are all "goodies" and we need them, but at just the right level — not too much and not too little.

Learn the Organs Involved in Homeostasis:

Hypothalamus
(some people call it the Thermoregulatory centre)

1) Contains receptors to monitor blood temperature and water content and then sends nerve impulses to the skin and to the pituitary gland.
2) It also monitors CO_2 levels.

The Brain

Pituitary Gland
Produces many vital hormones, including ADH, for controlling water content.

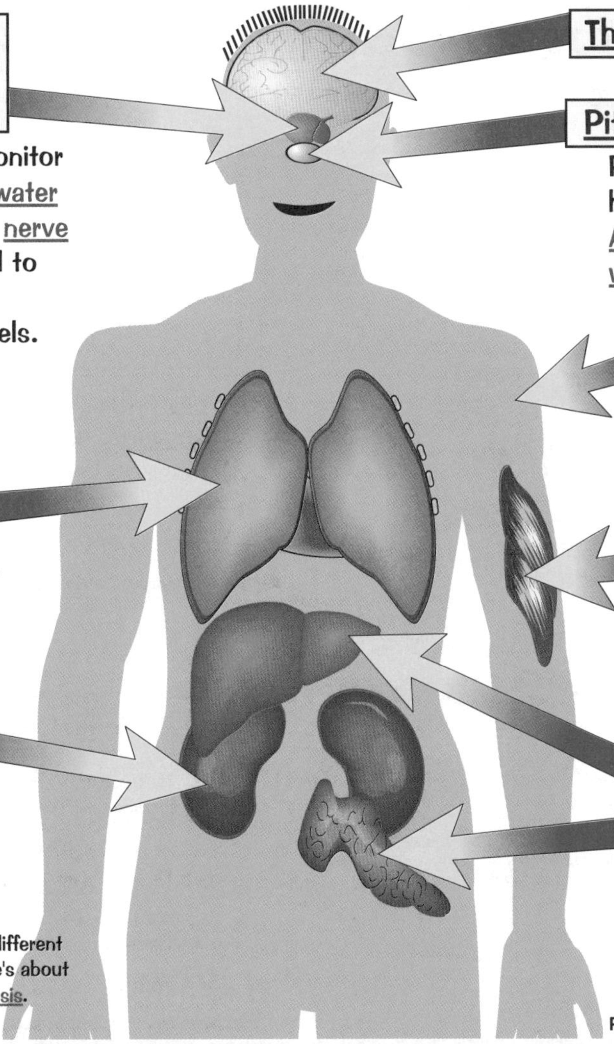

The Skin
This adjusts the body temperature, with the help of...

The Lungs
These remove CO_2 in exhaled air.

The Muscles
They can produce heat if necessary (by shivering).

The Kidneys
Remove urea in urine. They also adjust the ion and water content of the blood.

The liver
The pancreas
These two work together to adjust blood sugar level.

I hope you've clocked on that this is a different diagram from the one on P. 9. That one's about hormones — this one's about homeostasis.

Fingers *not* needed for homeostasis.

Learn about Homeostasis — and keep your cool...

This is all a bit technical. Homeostasis is really quite a complicated business. It's just a good job it does it automatically or we'd all be in real trouble. You still gotta learn it for your Exam though. Scribble.

Homeostasis

Controlling Our Body Temperature

All <u>enzymes</u> work best at a certain temperature. The enzymes in the human body work best at about <u>37°C</u>. To keep your enzymes at warm and toasty <u>37°C</u> your body does these things:

When you're too <u>cold</u> your body <u>shivers</u> (increasing your metabolism) to produce heat.

When you're too <u>hot</u> you produce <u>sweat</u> which cools you down.

Higher

1) There is a <u>thermoregulatory centre</u> in the <u>brain</u> which acts as your own <u>personal thermostat</u>.

2) It contains receptors that are sensitive to the blood temperature in the brain.

3) The thermoregulatory (there's that long word again) centre also receives impulses from the skin.

4) These impulses provide information about <u>skin temperature</u>.

Higher

The Skin has Three Tricks for Altering Body Temperature

1) The <u>thermoregulatory centre</u> senses changes and sends <u>nervous impulses</u> to the skin.

2) <u>The skin</u> then has <u>three ways</u> of <u>controlling body temperature</u> — using hairs, sweat and blood supply. Here's how they work:

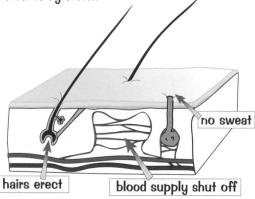

When you're TOO COLD:
1) <u>Hairs</u> stand on end to keep you warm.
2) <u>No sweat</u> is produced.
3) The <u>blood supply</u> to the skin <u>closes off</u>.
4) This is called <u>vasoconstriction</u>.

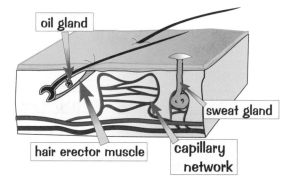

When you're TOO HOT:
1) <u>Hairs</u> lie flat.
2) <u>Sweat</u> is produced which evaporates to cool you down.
3) The <u>blood supply</u> to the skin opens up to release body heat.
4) This is called <u>vasodilation</u>.

So much to learn — don't let it get under your skin...

I can count about loads of important facts to learn on this page, plus a couple of suitably splendid diagrams. <u>Learn the headings</u> for each section, then <u>cover the page</u> and <u>scribble</u> out the details.

Section One — Life Processes

Kidneys

Kidneys basically act as filters to "clean the blood"

The kidneys perform three main roles:

> 1) Removal of urea from the blood.
>
> 2) Adjustment of ions in the blood.
>
> 3) Adjustment of water content of the blood.

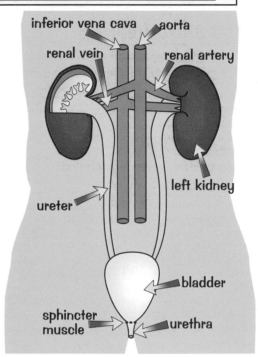

inferior vena cava — aorta

renal vein — renal artery

left kidney

ureter

bladder

sphincter muscle — urethra

1) Removal of Urea

1) Urea is produced in the liver.

2) Proteins can't be *stored* by the body so excess amino acids are *broken down* by the liver into fats and carbohydrates.

3) The *waste product* is urea which is passed into the blood to be filtered out by the kidneys. Urea is also lost partly in sweat. Urea is poisonous.

2) Adjustment of Ion (Salt) Content

1) Ions, such as sodium are taken into the body in food, and then absorbed into the blood.

2) Excess ions are removed by the kidneys. For example, a salty meal will contain far too much and the kidneys will remove the excess from the blood.

3) Some ions are also lost in sweat (which tastes salty, you'll have noticed).

4) But the important thing to remember is that the balance is always maintained by the kidneys.

3) Adjustment of Water Content

Water is *taken in* to the body as *food and drink* and is lost from the body in three ways:
>   1) in urine 2) in sweat 3) in breath

There's a need for the body to constantly balance the water coming in against the water going out. The amount lost in the *breath* is fairly *constant*, which means the water balance is between:
>   1) Liquids consumed
>   2) Amount sweated out
>   3) Amount dumped by the kidneys in the urine.

On a cold day, if you don't sweat, you'll produce more urine, which will be pale and dilute. On a hot day, you sweat a lot, your urine will be dark-coloured, concentrated and little of it. The water lost when it is hot has to be taken in as food and drink to restore the balance.

How Much Do You Know About Kidneys? — Let's See...

Phew. There's some stuff on this page isn't there. And it's all exciting stuff at that. The best way to learn all this stuff is the good ol' "mini-essay" method. Write down the headings first, and then try to fill in the rest of the information underneath — all without looking at the page, of course. Then go back and see what you missed. And if you did forget stuff, do it all again until you get it all spot-on.

Kidneys

Three Stages of Filtration in the Kidneys

1) Ultrafiltration:

1) A _high pressure_ is built up which _squeezes water_, _urea_, _ions_ and _glucose_ out of the blood and into the _kidney tubule_.
2) However, _big molecules_ like _proteins_ are _not squeezed out_. They stay in the blood.

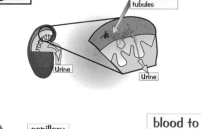

2) Reabsorption:

Useful substances are reabsorbed:
1) _All the sugar_ is reabsorbed.
   This involves the process of _active uptake_.
2) _Sufficient ions_ are reabsorbed. Excess ions are not.
   Active uptake is needed.
3) _Sufficient water_ is reabsorbed, according to the level of the hormone _ADH_ (see below).

3) Release of wastes:

1) All _urea_ and _excess ions and water_ are _not reabsorbed_.
2) These continue _out of the kidney_, into the ureter and down to the _bladder_ as _urine_.

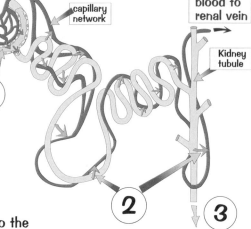

ADH (Antidiuretic Hormone) — Water Regulation

The brain _monitors the water content of the blood_ and instructs the _PITUITARY GLAND_ to release _ADH_ into the blood _accordingly_, as shown below:

Too Little Water in Blood

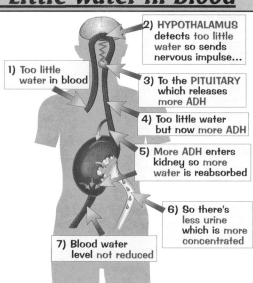

1) Too little water in blood

2) HYPOTHALAMUS detects too little water so sends nervous impulse...

3) To the PITUITARY which releases more ADH

4) Too little water but now more ADH

5) More ADH enters kidney so more water is reabsorbed

6) So there's less urine which is more concentrated

7) Blood water level not reduced

Too Much Water in Blood

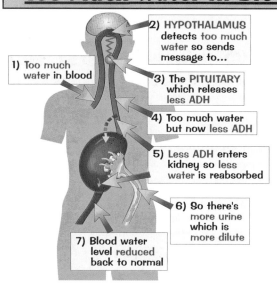

1) Too much water in blood

2) HYPOTHALAMUS detects too much water so sends message to...

3) The PITUITARY which releases less ADH

4) Too much water but now less ADH

5) Less ADH enters kidney so less water is reabsorbed

6) So there's more urine which is more dilute

7) Blood water level reduced back to normal

Phew — taking the mickey is much less complicated...

There's some tricky stuff on this page, that's for sure. It's definitely a perfect candidate for the exciting mini-essay method. Learn the headings, then _cover the page_, write them down, and then _scribble a mini-essay_ for each one. Then look back and see what you missed. _Then try again_. And learn the diagrams, until you can repeat them too.

Disease in Humans

There are two types of Micro-organism: Bacteria and Viruses

Micro-organisms are organisms which get inside you and make you feel ill. There are two main types:

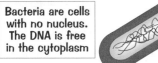

Bacteria are cells with no nucleus. The DNA is free in the cytoplasm

Bacillus Coccus Spirillum

Bacteria are Very Small Living Cells

1) These are <u>very small cells</u>, (about 1/100th the size of your body cells), which reproduce rapidly inside your body.

2) They make you feel ill by doing <u>two</u> things:
   a) <u>damaging</u> your <u>cells</u>   b) producing <u>toxins</u>.

3) Don't forget that some bacteria are <u>useful</u> if they're in the <u>right place</u>, like in your digestive system.

Viruses are not cells — they're much smaller

1) These are <u>not</u> cells. They are very very small — about 1/100th the size of a bacterium.

2) They make you feel ill by damaging your cells.

3) They <u>replicate themselves</u> by invading a cell and producing many <u>copies</u> of themselves.

4) The cell then <u>bursts</u>, releasing all the new viruses.

5) In this way they can reproduce <u>very quickly</u>.

A horrid Flu Virus

Three ways our bodies defend against micro-organisms

Micro-organisms can enter our bodies in different ways, but we do have some <u>defences</u>.

1) The Skin and Eyes

<u>Undamaged skin</u> is a very effective barrier against micro-organisms. If it gets damaged, the blood <u>clots</u> quickly to <u>seal cuts</u> and keep the micro-organisms out.
<u>Eyes</u> produce a chemical which <u>kills bacteria</u> on the surface of the eye.

2) The Digestive System

<u>Contaminated food</u> and <u>dirty water</u> allow micro-organisms to enter your body. The stomach produces strong <u>hydrochloric acid</u> which <u>kills</u> most micro-organisms which enter that way.

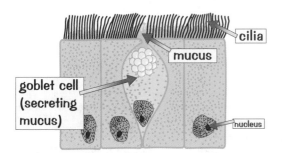

cili
mucus
goblet cell (secreting mucus)
nucleus

3) The Respiratory System

The whole <u>respiratory tract</u> (nasal passage, trachea and lungs) is lined with <u>mucus</u> and <u>cilia</u> which catch <u>dust</u> and <u>bacteria</u> before they reach the lungs.

Disease in Humans

Once micro-organisms have entered our bodies they will <u>reproduce rapidly</u> unless they are destroyed. Your '<u>immune system</u>' does just that, and <u>white blood cells</u> are the most important part of it.

Your Immune System: White blood cells

They travel around in your blood and crawl into every part of you, constantly <u>patrolling</u> for micro-organisms. When they come across an invading micro-organism they have <u>three lines of attack</u>:

1) Consuming Them

White blood cells can <u>engulf</u> foreign cells and <u>digest</u> them.

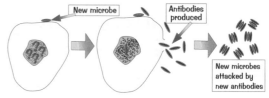

Microbes

White Blood Cell

2) Producing Antibodies

When your white blood cells come across a <u>foreign cell</u> they will start to produce proteins called <u>antibodies</u> to kill the new invading cells. The antibodies are then produced <u>rapidly</u> and flow all round the body to kill all <u>similar</u> bacteria or viruses.

New microbe

Antibodies produced

New microbes attacked by new antibodies

3) Producing Antitoxins

<u>Antitoxins</u> counter the effect of any <u>poisons</u> (toxins) produced by the <u>invading bacteria</u>.

Immunisation — Getting antibodies ready for attack

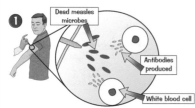

Dead measles microbes

Antibodies produced

White blood cell

If measles microbes try to attack

No time off school...

Antibodies

They are recognised quickly and attacked

1) Once your white cells have produced antibodies to tackle a new strain of bacteria or virus you are said to have developed "<u>natural immunity</u>" to it.

2) This means if the <u>same micro-organisms</u> attack again they'll be killed by the <u>antibodies</u> you already have for them, and you <u>won't get ill</u>.

3) The trouble is when a <u>new</u> micro-organism appears, it takes your white blood cells a few days to produce the antibodies to deal with them and in that time you can get <u>very ill</u>.

4) There are plenty of diseases which can make you very ill indeed (e.g. polio, tetanus, measles) and only <u>immunisation</u> stops you getting them.

5) Immunisation involves injecting <u>dead</u> micro-organisms into you. This causes your body to produce <u>antibodies</u> to attack them, even though they're dead. They can do no <u>harm</u> to you because they're dead.

6) If <u>live</u> micro-organisms of the same type appeared after that, they'd be <u>killed immediately</u> by the antibodies which you have already developed against them. Cool.

Antibiotics kill Bacteria but NOT Viruses

1) <u>Antibiotics</u> are drugs that kill <u>bacteria</u> without killing your own body cells.
2) They are very useful for clearing up infections that your body is having <u>trouble</u> with.
3) However they don't kill <u>viruses</u>.
   <u>Flu and colds</u> are caused by <u>viruses</u> and basically, you're on your own, pal.
4) There are <u>no drugs</u> to kill <u>viruses</u> and you just have to <u>wait</u> for your body to deal with it and <u>suffer</u> in the meantime.
5) Still, it's better than being bitten by a rat flea.

A horrid Flu Virus

An even more horrid Rat Flea

It's Grisly Stuff, but worth learning just the same...

Two pages this time, and definitely 'mini-essay' material. There are three main sections, with several subsections. Do a <u>mini-essay</u> on each subsection and then <u>check</u> what you forgot.

Drugs

1) Drugs are substances which alter the way the body works. Some drugs are useful of course, for example antibiotics such as penicillin. However there are many drugs which are <u>dangerous</u> if misused, and many of them are <u>addictive</u> or "habit-forming".
2) The loss of control and judgement caused by many drugs can easily lead to <u>death</u> from various other causes, e.g. getting HIV or hepatitis from used needles, choking on vomit... Horrible, horrible things.

There are two types of Addiction — Chemical and Psychological

1) There's a difference between true <u>chemical addiction</u> and <u>psychological addiction</u>.
2) In <u>chemical addiction</u> the body becomes adjusted to the constant presence of the drug in the system. If the drug is withdrawn, there are various <u>unpleasant physical withdrawal symptoms</u>: fevers, hallucinations, nausea, and the shakes.
3) <u>Psychological addiction</u> is where the person "feels the need" to keep taking the drug.

Stimulants

1) <u>Stimulants</u> tend to make the nervous system generally more alert and "awake".
2) Caffeine is a mild stimulant found in tea and coffee. It's pretty harmless. Few lives are wrecked by obsessive tea-drinking.
3) However, amphetamine and methedrine are also stimulants.
4) Strong stimulants like these produce a feeling of boundless energy, but the person experiences <u>serious depression</u> if they stop taking it, so an unhealthy <u>dependence</u> develops all too easily. Continued use can lead to hallucinations and <u>changes in personality</u>.

<u>Depressants</u> tend to slow down the responses of the nervous system, causing <u>slow reactions</u> and poor judgement of speed, distances, etc. See "Alcohol" on the next page.

Pain Killers — Aspirin, Heroin and Morphine

1) Heroin is a <u>particularly nasty</u> drug causing a serious <u>deterioration</u> in personality and as the addiction grows the person's whole life <u>degenerates</u> into a <u>desperate struggle</u> to obtain money for their daily heroin requirement, often resulting in a <u>sad life of crime</u> to pay for it.
2) Morphine is also highly <u>addictive</u>.
3) Aspirin is a useful painkiller for many minor illnesses, but its overuse has <u>harmful effects</u>.

Solvents

1) Solvents are found in a variety of "household" items e.g. glues, paints etc.
2) They are <u>dangerous</u> and have many <u>damaging effects</u> on your body and personality.
3) They cause hallucinations and adversely affect personality and behaviour.
4) They cause <u>damage</u> to the <u>lungs</u>, <u>brain</u>, <u>liver</u> and <u>kidney</u>.

Learn about these drugs and then forget them...

Anyone with half a brain avoids these drugs like they do <u>rat fleas</u>.
Enjoy your life, instead of being a sucker.

Drugs

1) Alcohol and tobacco are the two main (non-medical) drugs which are legal in this country.
2) But don't be fooled. They can do you a lot of harm just like the other drugs can.

Alcohol

1) The main effect of alcohol is to reduce the activity of the nervous system. The positive aspect of this is that it makes us feel less inhibited, and there's no doubt that alcohol in moderation helps people to socialise and relax with each other.
2) However, if you let alcohol take over, it can wreck your life. And it does. It wrecks a lot of people's lives. You've got to control it.
3) Once alcohol starts to take over someone's life there are many harmful effects:
   a) Alcohol is basically poisonous. Too much drinking will cause severe damage to the liver and the brain leading to liver disease and a noticeable drop in brain function.
   b) Too much alcohol impairs judgement which can cause accidents, and it can also severely affect the person's work and home life.
   c) Serious dependency on alcohol will eventually lead to loss of job, loss of income and the start of a severe downward spiral.

Smoking Tobacco

Smoking is no good to anyone except the cigarette companies.
And once you've started smoking there's no going back. It's a one way trip pal.

And you'll notice that smokers are no happier than non-smokers, even when they're smoking. What may start off as something "different" to do, rapidly becomes something they have to do, just to feel OK. But non-smokers feel just as OK without spending £20 or more each week and wrecking their health into the bargain.

And why do people start smoking? To look the part, that's why. They have an image in their head of how they want to appear and smoking seems the perfect fashion accessory.

Well just remember, it's a one way trip. You might think it makes you look cool at 16, but will it still seem the perfect fashion accessory when you're 20 with a new group of friends who don't smoke? Nope. Too late. You're stuck with it.

And by the time you're 60 it'll have cost you over £40,000. Enough to buy a Ferrari or a new house. That's quite an expensive fashion accessory.
Smoking? Cool? Oh yeah — it's about as cool as cool can be, I'd say.

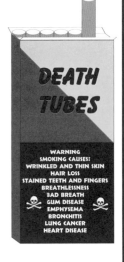

DEATH TUBES

WARNING
SMOKING CAUSES:
WRINKLED AND THIN SKIN
HAIR LOSS
STAINED TEETH AND FINGERS
BREATHLESSNESS
BAD BREATH
GUM DISEASE
EMPHYSEMA
BRONCHITIS
LUNG CANCER
HEART DISEASE

Oh and by the way...

Tobacco smoke does this inside your body:
1) It coats the inside of your lungs with tar so they become hideously inefficient.
2) It covers the cilia in tar preventing them from getting bacteria out of your lungs.
3) It causes disease of the heart and blood vessels, leading to heart attacks and strokes.
4) It causes lung cancer. Out of every ten lung cancer patients, nine of them smoke.

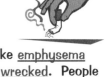

Smoking stains teeth yellow.
Brushing doesn't really get rid of it.

5) It causes severe loss of lung function leading to diseases like emphysema and bronchitis, in which the inside of the lungs is basically wrecked. People with severe bronchitis can't manage even a brisk walk, because their lungs can't get enough oxygen into the blood. It eventually kills over 20,000 people in Britain every year.
6) Carbon monoxide in tobacco smoke stops haemoglobin carrying as much oxygen. In pregnant women this deprives the fetus of oxygen leading to a small baby at birth. In short, "smoking chokes your baby".
7) But this is the best bit. The effect of the nicotine is negligible — other than to make you addicted to it. It doesn't make you high — just dependent. Great. Fantastic.

Learn the Numbered Points for your Exam...

It's the disease aspects they concentrate on most in the Exams. Learn the rest for a nice life.

Revision Summary for Section One

Well, that's Human Biology pretty much in a nutshell. And some of it can be quite hard to understand. But it's all worth points in the Exam, and what do points mean? Prizes! These questions are designed to test what you know — they really are the best way of revising. Keep trying these questions, and for any you can't do, look back in Section One and learn the answer to it for next time.

1) Sketch an animal cell.
2) Fill in the blanks in this sequence: .... → .... → organ → organism:
3) Sketch the digestive system and put ten labels on it. Give two details for each labelled part.
4) Draw a diagram of a peristaltic squeeze and label the different types of tissue, with their use.
5) Sketch a villus, and say what it's for. Point out the three main features of villi.
6) What *exactly* do enzymes do in the digestive system?
7) List the three digestive enzymes, which foods they act on, and what they produce.
8) What *two* things does bile do? Where is it produced? Where does it enter the system?
9) What are the three "big" food molecules, and which kind of foods are each of them found in?
10) What small molecules are they each broken down into in the digestive system?
11) Sketch a diagram showing what then happens to the small molecules.
12) Sketch a red blood cell and give five details about it. Then do the same for a white blood cell.
13) List ten things that are carried in the plasma. Sketch some platelets. What do they do all day?
14) Draw a diagram showing the main parts of the nervous system.
15) List the five sense organs and say what kind of receptors each one has.
16) What are effectors? What two things constitute the central nervous system?
17) What are the three types of neurone? Draw a detailed diagram of a typical neurone.
18) Describe how a synapse works and how a reflex arc works.
19) Draw a full diagram of an eye with all labels and details.
20) Describe how the eye adjusts for light and dark, and to focus on near and distant objects.
21) Draw a diagram of the body and label the five places where hormones are produced.
22) Give a definition of a hormone. Give four differences between nerves and hormones.
23) Give brief details of the four stages in the female menstrual cycle.
24) Sketch the diagram showing the state of the uterus lining at each stage.
25) Name the hormones that are used: a) to promote fertility   b) in "The Pill".
26) What are the three main hormones involved in the female menstrual cycle?
27) Define homeostasis. What are the six bodily levels involved?
28) On a diagram of the body, show the 8 organs involved in homeostasis, and say what each does to help.
29) What temperature do our bodily enzymes like?
30) Which organ detects body temperature? How does it tell the skin about it?
31) Draw diagrams showing the three things the skin does when we're a) too hot b) too cold.
32) What is the basic function of the kidneys? What *three* particular things do they deal with?
33) Explain in detail exactly what the kidney does in relation to each of these three things.
34) Explain how ADH is involved in regulating the water content of the blood.
35) What are the two types of micro-organism? How big are they compared to a human cell?
36) How exactly do bacteria make you feel ill? What do viruses do inside you to reproduce?
37) Name four ways our bodies can stop micro-organisms entering.
38) What is meant by your "immune system"? What is the most important part of it?
39) List the three ways that white blood cells deal with invading micro-organisms.
40) Give full details of the process of immunisation. What are antibiotics? What will they work on?
41) What are the two types of addiction to drugs?
42) List three different types of "drug" with examples of each. List the dangers of each type.
43) Explain the dangers of drinking alcohol. Explain why smoking is just *so cool* — not.
44) List in detail all six major health problems that result from smoking.

Variation in Plants and Animals

1) Young plants and animals obviously <u>resemble</u> their <u>parents</u>. In other words they show <u>similar characteristics</u> such as jagged leaves or perfect eyebrows.

2) However young animals and plants can also <u>differ</u> from their parents and each other.

3) These similarities and differences lead to <u>variation</u> within the same species.

4) The word "<u>variation</u>" sounds far too fancy for its own good. All it means is how animals or plants of the same species <u>look</u> or <u>behave</u> slightly different from each other. You know, a bit <u>taller</u> or a bit <u>fatter</u> or a bit more <u>scary-to-look-at</u> etc.

There are <u>two</u> causes of variation: <u>Genetic Variation</u> and <u>Environmental Variation</u>.

Read on, and learn...

1) *Genetic variation*

 You'll know this already.

1) <u>All animals</u> (including humans) are bound to be slightly different from each other because their <u>genes</u> are slightly different.

2) Genes are the code inside all your cells which determine how your body turns out. We all end up with a slightly different set of genes.

3) The <u>exceptions</u> to that rule are <u>identical twins</u>, because their genes are <u>exactly the same</u>.

But even identical twins are never <u>completely identical</u> — and that's because of the other factor:

2) *Environmental Variation is shown up by Identical Twins*

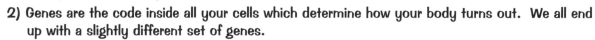

If you're not sure what "<u>environment</u>" means, think of it as "<u>upbringing</u>" instead — it's pretty much the same thing — how and where you were "brought up".

Since we know the <u>twins' genes</u> are <u>identical</u>, any differences between them <u>must</u> be caused by slight differences <u>in their environment</u> throughout their lives.

<u>Twins</u> give us a fairly good idea of how important the <u>two factors</u> (genes and environment) are, compared to each other — at least for animals.

Four animal characteristics affected by genes and not environment are:

1) <u>Eye colour</u>.

2) <u>Hair colour</u> in most animals (but not humans where vanity plays a big part).

3) <u>Inherited diseases</u> like haemophilia, cystic fibrosis, etc.

4) <u>Blood group</u>.   *And that's about it! So <u>learn those four</u> in case they ask you.*

 Plants always show much <u>greater variation</u> due to differences in their environment than animals do. For example, plants may grow <u>twice as big</u> or <u>twice as fast</u> due to <u>fairly modest</u> changes in environment such as the amount of <u>sunlight</u> or <u>rainfall</u> they're getting, or how <u>warm</u> it is or what the <u>soil</u> is like.

A cat, on the other hand, born and bred in the North of Scotland, could be sent out to live in equatorial Africa and would show no significant changes — it would look the same, eat the same, and it would probably still puke up everywhere.

Combinations of Genetic and Environmental Variation

<u>Everything else</u> is determined by <u>a mixture</u> of <u>genetic</u> and <u>environmental</u> factors:
<u>Body weight</u>, <u>height</u>, <u>skin colour</u>, <u>condition of teeth</u>, <u>academic or athletic prowess</u>, etc. etc.

Don't let Everything get to you — just learn the facts...

There are three sections on this page. After you think you've learnt it all, <u>cover the page</u> and do a "<u>mini-essay</u>" on each of the sections. Then <u>check back</u> and see what important points you missed.

Ordinary Cell Division: Mitosis

If you're going to get <u>anywhere</u> with this topic you definitely need to learn what and where <u>chromosomes</u> are, and what and where a <u>gene</u> is. If you don't get that sorted out first, then anything else you read about them won't make a lot of sense to you — <u>will it</u>.

Every Cell contains 23 pairs of Chromosomes

1) Every one of our body cells has <u>23 pairs</u> of chromosomes in its nucleus.

2) These chromosomes contain all the genetic information needed to make us.

3) Each pair of chromosomes is different and has a number — so we have two No. 19 chromosomes, two No.12s etc.

4) The chromosomes are made from DNA, and are divided into short sections called <u>genes</u>.

5) Each gene has information about one particular thing, e.g. <u>hair colour</u>.

Mitosis — Ordinary Cell Division

"Mitosis is when a cell reproduces itself <u>by splitting</u> to form <u>two identical offspring</u>."

The really riveting part of the whole process is how the chromosomes split inside the cell. Learn and enjoy...

The <u>double arms</u> are already <u>duplicates</u> of each other.

Chromosomes line up along the centre and then <u>the cell fibres pull them apart</u>.

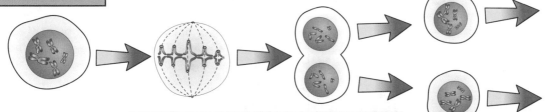

Membranes form around the two sets of chromosome threads. These become the <u>nuclei</u> of the two daughter cells.

(Note the single chromosome threads have now duplicated themselves — see below.)

Higher

Mitosis and Asexual Reproduction

<u>Mitosis</u> produces new cells <u>identical</u> to the original cell.

This is how all plants and animals <u>grow</u> and <u>replace</u> dead or damaged cells.

Their cells <u>divide</u> and <u>multiply</u> by the process of <u>mitosis</u>. However some organisms also <u>reproduce</u> using mitosis, <u>bacteria</u> being a good example. This is known as <u>asexual</u> reproduction. Here's a <u>definition</u> of it, for you to learn:

> In <u>asexual reproduction</u> there is only <u>one</u> parent, and the offspring therefore have <u>exactly the same genes</u> as the parent (i.e. they're clones — see P.32).

This is because all the cells in <u>both</u> parent and offspring were produced by <u>mitosis</u> from one another, so they must all have <u>identical genes</u> in their cell nuclei.

Some <u>plants</u> reproduce asexually, e.g. potatoes, strawberries and daffodils.

Now that I have your undivided attention...

You need to <u>learn</u> the definition of <u>mitosis</u> and the sequence of diagrams, and also the definition of <u>asexual reproduction</u>. Now <u>cover the page</u> and <u>scribble down</u> the two definitions and sketch out the sequence of diagrams — <u>don't waste time</u> with neatness — just find out if you've <u>learnt it all</u> yet.

Gamete Production: Meiosis

You thought mitosis was exciting. Hah! You ain't seen nothing yet. <u>Meiosis</u> is the other type of cell division. It only happens in the <u>reproductive organs</u> (ovaries and testes).

> Meiosis produces "<u>cells which have half the proper number of chromosomes</u>".
> Such cells are also known as "<u>haploid gametes</u>".

These cells are "genetically different" from each other because the genes all get <u>shuffled up</u> during meiosis and each gamete only gets <u>half</u> of them, selected at random.
Confused? I'm not surprised. But fear not, coz...   ....well worse things happen at sea...
The diagrams below will make it a lot clearer — but you have to <u>study</u> them pretty hard.

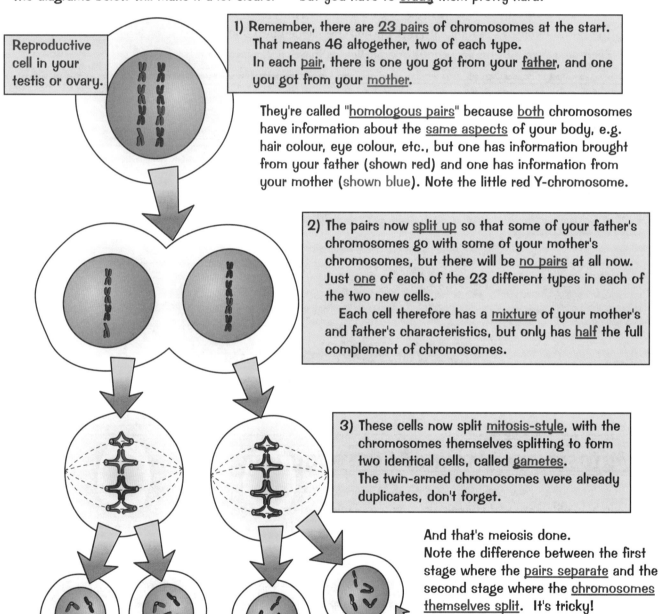

Reproductive cell in your testis or ovary.

1) Remember, there are <u>23 pairs</u> of chromosomes at the start. That means 46 altogether, two of each type. In each <u>pair</u>, there is one you got from your <u>father</u>, and one you got from your <u>mother</u>.

They're called "<u>homologous pairs</u>" because <u>both</u> chromosomes have information about the <u>same aspects</u> of your body, e.g. hair colour, eye colour, etc., but one has information brought from your father (shown red) and one has information from your mother (shown blue). Note the little red Y-chromosome.

2) The pairs now <u>split up</u> so that some of your father's chromosomes go with some of your mother's chromosomes, but there will be <u>no pairs</u> at all now. Just <u>one</u> of each of the 23 different types in each of the two new cells.
   Each cell therefore has a <u>mixture</u> of your mother's and father's characteristics, but only has <u>half</u> the full complement of chromosomes.

3) These cells now split <u>mitosis-style</u>, with the chromosomes themselves splitting to form two identical cells, called <u>gametes</u>.
   The twin-armed chromosomes were already duplicates, don't forget.

And that's meiosis done.
Note the difference between the first stage where the <u>pairs separate</u> and the second stage where the <u>chromosomes themselves split</u>. It's tricky!

<u>Gametes</u>
i.e. sperm cells or egg cells.

Meiosis? Not even remotely scary...
There's a few tricky words in there which don't help — especially if you just ignore them...
The only way to <u>learn</u> this page is by constant reference to the diagram. Make sure you can sketch all the parts of it <u>from memory</u> and <u>scribble notes</u> to explain each stage. Even so, it's still difficult to understand it all, never mind remember it. But that's what you gotta do!

Fertilisation: The Meeting of Gametes

There are 23 Pairs of Human Chromosomes

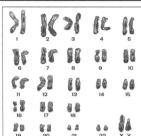

They are well known and numbered. In every <u>cell nucleus</u> we have <u>two</u> of each type. The diagram shows the 23 pairs of chromosomes from a human cell. <u>One</u> chromosome in <u>each pair</u> is inherited from each of our parents. Normal body cells have 46 chromosomes, in <u>23 homologous pairs</u>.

Remember, "<u>homologous</u>" means that the two chromosomes in each pair are <u>equivalent</u> to each other. In other words, the number 19 chromosomes from both your parents <u>pair off together</u>, as do the number 17s etc. What you <u>don't get</u> is the number 12 chromosome from one parent pairing off with, say, the number 5 chromosome from the other.

Reproductive Cells undergo Meiosis to Produce Gametes:

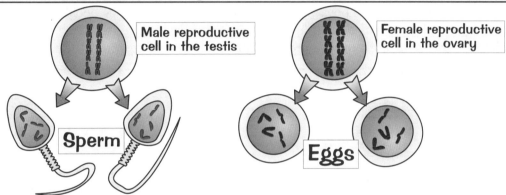

Male reproductive cell in the testis

Female reproductive cell in the ovary

Sperm

Eggs

The <u>gametes</u> remember, only have <u>one chromosome</u> to describe each bit of you, <u>one copy</u> of each of the chromosomes numbered 1 to 23. But a <u>normal cell</u> needs <u>two</u> chromosomes of each type — one from <u>each parent</u>, so...

Fertilisation is the Joining Together of the Gametes

Here's a mouthful of a <u>definition</u> for you to learn:

> **FERTILISATION** is the fusion of haploid male and female gametes, restoring the diploid number of chromosomes in a zygote.

Put simply fertilisation is when the <u>sperm</u> and the <u>egg</u>, with <u>23 chromosomes each</u>, join together to form an offspring with a full <u>46 chromosomes</u>. You've got to learn the posh <u>definition</u> though.

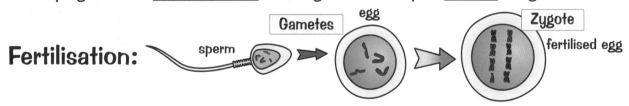

Fertilisation:

sperm

Gametes

egg

Zygote

fertilised egg

When the gametes **FUSE** the 23 single chromosomes in one gamete <u>will all pair off</u> with their appropriate "partner chromosomes" from the other gamete to form the full 23 pairs again, No.4 with No.4, No.13 with No.13 etc. etc. Don't forget, the two chromosomes in a pair both contain the <u>same basic genes</u>, e.g. for hair colour, etc.

The resulting offspring will then receive its <u>outward characteristics</u> as a <u>mixture</u> from the <u>two</u> sets of chromosomes, so it will <u>inherit features</u> from <u>both parents</u>. Pretty cool, eh.

It should all be starting to come together now...

If you go through these last two pages you should see how the two processes, meiosis and fertilisation, are kind of opposite. Practise <u>sketching out</u> the sequence of diagrams, with notes, for both pages till it all sinks in. Nice, innit.

Girl or Boy? — X and Y Chromosomes

There are 23 matched pairs of chromosomes in every human cell. You'll notice the 23rd pair are labelled XY. They're the two chromosomes that decide whether you turn out <u>male or female</u>. They're called the X and Y chromosomes because they look like an X and a Y.

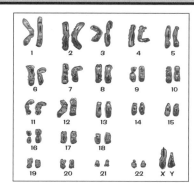

> <u>All men</u> have <u>an X</u> and <u>a Y</u> chromosome: XY
> <u>The Y chromosome is dominant</u> and causes <u>male characteristics</u>.
>
> <u>All women</u> have <u>two X chromosomes</u>:   XX
> The XX combination allows <u>female characteristics</u> to develop.

The diagram below shows the way the male XY chromosomes and female XX chromosomes split up to form the <u>gametes</u> (eggs or sperms), and then combine together at <u>fertilisation</u>.

The criss–cross lines show all the <u>possible</u> ways the X and Y chromosomes <u>could</u> combine. Remember, <u>only one of these</u> would actually happen for any offspring.

What the diagram shows us is the <u>relative probability</u> of each type of zygote (offspring) occurring.

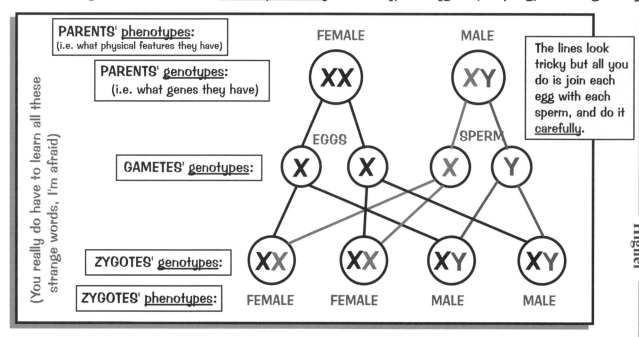

PARENTS' phenotypes:
(i.e. what physical features they have)

PARENTS' genotypes:
(i.e. what genes they have)

GAMETES' genotypes:

ZYGOTES' genotypes:

ZYGOTES' phenotypes:

FEMALE   MALE

The lines look tricky but all you do is join each egg with each sperm, and do it <u>carefully</u>.

(You really do have to learn all these strange words, I'm afraid)

EGGS   SPERM

FEMALE   FEMALE   MALE   MALE

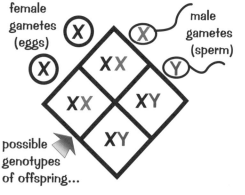

female gametes (eggs)

male gametes (sperm)

possible genotypes of offspring...

...two males (XY) and two females (XX).

The other way of doing this is with a <u>checkerboard</u> type diagram. If you don't understand how it works, ask "Teach" to explain it. The <u>pairs of letters</u> in the middle show the <u>genotypes</u> of the possible offspring.

Both diagrams show that there'll be the same proportion of male and female offspring, because there are <u>two XX results</u> and <u>two XY results</u>.

Don't forget that this <u>50:50 ratio</u> is only a <u>probability</u>. If you had four kids they <u>could</u> all be <u>boys</u> — yes I know, terrifying isn't it.

<u>How can it take all that just to say it's a 50:50 chance...</u>

Make sure you know all about X and Y chromosomes and who has what combination. The diagrams are real important. Practise reproducing them until you can do it <u>effortlessly</u>.

Monohybrid Crosses: Terminology

"Hey man, like *monohybrid crosses*, yeah right... ...so like, *what does it mean*, man?"   Just this, pal:

Breeding <u>two plants</u> or <u>animals</u>, who have <u>one gene different</u>, to see what you <u>get</u>.

It's always best done with a diagram like either of these:

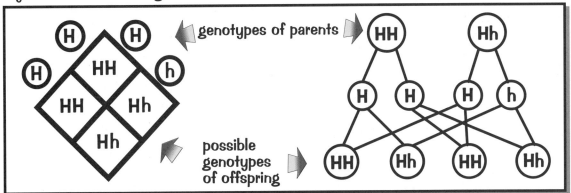

But first learn all these technical terms — it's real difficult to follow what's going on if you don't:

1) allele

— this is just another name for a <u>gene</u>. If you have two <u>different versions</u> of a <u>gene</u>, like H and h, then you have to call them <u>alleles</u> instead of genes.

2) dominant and recessive

— self explanatory. A dominant allele <u>dominates</u> a recessive allele.

3) genotype and phenotype

— <u>genotype</u> is just what <u>'type o' genes'</u> you've got, e.g. HH, Hh, or hh.
<u>Phenotype</u> sounds a lot like genotype but, irritatingly, is nothing like it at all.
Genotype is always a pair of letters like Hh, whilst <u>phenotype</u> is what <u>physical characteristics</u> result from the genotype, like "blue hair" or "big leaves" or "maleness".

4) "Parental", "F1" and "F2" generations

— pretty obvious. The two <u>originals</u> that you cross are the <u>parental generation</u>, their <u>kids</u> are the <u>F1 generation</u> and the <u>"grandchildren"</u> are the <u>F2 generation</u>. Easy peasy.

5) homozygous and heterozygous

— *"Homo-"* means <u>*"same kinda things"*</u>, *"Hetero-"* means <u>*"different kinda things"*</u>.
They stick <u>"-zygous"</u> on the end to show we're talking about <u>genes</u>, (rather than any other aspect of Biology), and also just to make it <u>sound more complicated</u>, I'm certain of it. So...

> "<u>Homozygous recessive</u>" is the descriptive 'shorthand' (hah!) for this: hh
> "<u>Homozygous dominant</u>" is the 'shorthand' for   HH
> "<u>Heterozygous</u>" is the 'shorthand' for   Hh
> "A <u>Homozygote</u>" or "a <u>Heterozygote</u>" are how you refer to people with such genes.

Let's try out the brilliant descriptive 'shorthand' shall we:

"Alexander is homozygous recessive for the baldness gene" is <u>so much easier</u> to say and understand than   *"Alex is bb".*   Hmm, well, that's Biology for you.

Now it's time to homologate your intellectual stimuli...

You can't beat a fewdal big fancyfold wordsmiths to make things crystally clearasil, can you...
Anyway, half the Exam marks are for knowing the fancy words <u>so just keep learning 'em!</u>

Monohybrid Crosses: Hamsters

Cross-breeding Hamsters

It can be all too easy to find yourself cross-breeding hamsters, some with normal hair and a mild disposition and others with wild scratty hair and a leaning towards crazy acrobatics.

Let's say that the gene which causes the crazy nature is <u>recessive</u>, so we use a <u>small "h"</u> for it, whilst normal (boring) behaviour is due to a <u>dominant gene</u>, so we represent it with a <u>capital "H"</u>.
1) A <u>crazy hamster</u> must have the <u>genotype</u>: hh.
2) However, a <u>normal hamster</u> can have <u>two possible genotypes</u>: HH or Hh.
  This is pretty important — it's the basic difference between dominant and recessive genes:

> To display <u>recessive characteristics</u> you must have <u>both alleles recessive</u>, hh, (i.e. be "homozygous recessive")
>
> But to display <u>dominant characteristics</u> you can be <u>either</u> HH ("homozygous dominant") or Hh ("heterozygous").

It's only that difference which makes monohybrid crosses even <u>remotely</u> interesting. If hh gave crazy hamsters, HH gave normal hamsters and Hh something in between, it'd all be pretty dull.

An Almost Unbearably Exciting Example

Let's take a thoroughbred crazy hamster, genotype hh, with a thoroughbred normal hamster, genotype HH, and cross breed them. You must learn this whole diagram thoroughly, till you can do it all yourself:

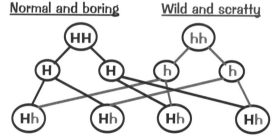

If two of these F1 generation now breed they will produce the F2 generation:

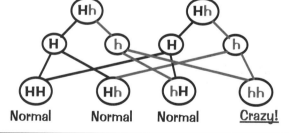

This gives a <u>3 : 1 ratio</u> of Normal to Crazy offspring in the F2 generation.
Remember that "<u>results</u>" like this are only <u>probabilities</u>. It doesn't mean it'll happen.
(Most likely, you'll end up trying to contain a mini-riot of nine lunatic baby hamsters.)

See how those fancy words start to roll off the tongue...

The diagram and all its fancy words need to be second nature to you. So practise writing it out <u>from memory</u> until you get it all right. Because when you can do one — <u>you can do 'em all</u>.

Genetic Disorders

Cystic Fibrosis is caused by a Recessive Allele

1) *Cystic Fibrosis* is a <u>genetic disorder</u> caused by a <u>defective gene</u> inherited from parents.
2) The body produces a lot of <u>thick sticky mucus</u> in the <u>lungs</u>, causing <u>chest infections</u>, and in the <u>pancreas</u>, causing <u>digestive problems</u>.
3) <u>Physiotherapy and antibiotics</u> clear them up but slowly the sufferer becomes more and more ill.

Here's the <u>genetics</u> behind cystic fibrosis:
The gene which causes cystic fibrosis is a <u>recessive gene</u>, c, carried by about <u>1 person in 20</u>.

If both parents are carriers there's a <u>1 in 4 chance</u> of their child being a sufferer, as shown in the diagram.

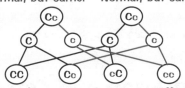

PARENTS' phenotype: Normal, but carrier   Normal, but carrier
PARENTS' genotype: Cc   Cc
GAMETES' genotype: C   c   C   c
ZYGOTES' genotype: CC   Cc   cC   cc
ZYGOTES' phenotype: normal   carrier   carrier   sufferer

So is Sickle Cell Anaemia

1) This disorder causes the <u>red blood cells</u> to be shaped like <u>sickles</u> instead of the normal round shape. They then get <u>stuck</u> in the capillaries which deprives body cells of <u>oxygen</u>.
2) It's unpleasant and painful and sufferers are at risk of dying young.

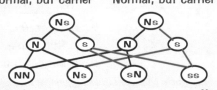

normal cell   sickle cell

The genetics are <u>identical</u> to <u>Cystic Fibrosis</u> because both disorders are caused by a <u>recessive allele</u>. Hence if <u>both</u> parents are carriers there's a <u>1 in 4 chance</u> each child will develop it.

PARENTS' phenotype: Normal, but carrier   Normal, but carrier
PARENTS' genotype: Ns   Ns
GAMETES' genotype: N   s   N   s
ZYGOTES' genotype: NN   Ns   sN   ss
ZYGOTES' phenotype: normal   carrier   carrier   sufferer

Huntington's Chorea is caused by a Dominant Allele

1) <u>Unlike</u> Cystic Fibrosis this disorder is caused by a <u>dominant allele</u>. This results in a <u>50% chance</u> of each child inheriting the disorder if just <u>one parent</u> is a carrier. Seriously grim odds.
2) The "<u>carrier</u>" parent will be a <u>sufferer</u> too, since the allele is dominant, but the symptoms don't show until after the age of 40, by which time the allele has been passed on to <u>children</u>.
3) The disorder isn't nice, resulting in shaking, erratic body movements and severe mental deterioration.

Note: <u>If</u> one parent is a (heterozygous) <u>sufferer</u>, there's a <u>2 in 4 chance</u> of each of his or her children having the disorder.

PARENTS' PHENOTYPE: Carrier/sufferer   normal
PARENTS' GENOTYPE: Hn   nn
GAMETES' GENOTYPE: H   n   n   n
ZYGOTES' GENOTYPE: Hn   Hn   nn   nn
ZYGOTES' PHENOTYPE: Sufferer   Sufferer   normal   normal

And so is Polydactyly

1) Polydactyly is a disorder that causes the person to have <u>extra fingers</u> and <u>extra toes</u>.
2) It's caused by a <u>dominant allele</u> so the genetic diagrams are the same as Huntington's Chorea. The disorder isn't fatal and doesn't affect reproduction so sufferers pass on the Polydactyly genes to their children as follows:

There's a <u>50%</u> chance of each child inheriting the disorder if just <u>one parent</u> is a (heterozygous) carrier and a <u>75%</u> chance if both parents are carriers.

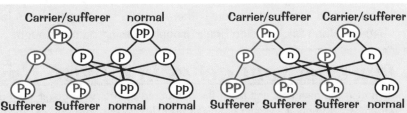

Carrier/sufferer   normal   Carrier/sufferer   Carrier/sufferer
Pp   PP   Pn   Pn
P   P   P   P   P   n   P   n
Pp   Pp   PP   PP   PP   Pn   Pn   nn
Sufferer   Sufferer   normal   normal   Sufferer   Sufferer   Sufferer   normal

Section Two — Genetics and Evolution

Mutations

Mutation sounds like a word to mean only bad things... and most of the time it is, but mutations are also what makes evolution happen — without them we'd still be goo in the primordial soup. No exams though.

A MUTATION is a change in a gene or the number of chromosomes in a cell which leads to genetic variation.

Mutations Show up as a Strange New Characteristic

1) A mutation occurs when an organism develops with some strange new characteristic that no other member of the species has had before.
2) For example if someone was born with blue hair it would be caused by a mutation.
3) Some mutations are beneficial, but most are disastrous (e.g. blue hair).

Radiation and Certain Chemicals cause Mutations

Mutations occur "naturally", probably caused by "natural" background radiation (from the sun and rocks etc.) or just the laws of chance that every now and then a chromosome doesn't quite copy itself properly.

However the chance of mutation is increased by exposing yourself:

1) To nuclear radiation, i.e. alpha, beta and gamma radiation. This is sometimes called ionising radiation because it creates ions (charged particles) as it passes through stuff.

2) To X-rays and Ultraviolet light, which are the highest-frequency parts of the electromagnetic spectrum (together with gamma rays).

3) To certain chemicals which are known to cause mutations. Such chemicals are called mutagens! If the mutations produce cancer then the chemicals are often called carcinogens.

Cigarette smoke contains chemical mutagens (or carcinogens)... (I'm sayin' nowt — See P.18.)

Most Mutations are Harmful — e.g. Cancer

1) If a mutation occurs in reproductive cells, then the young may develop abnormally or die young.
2) If a mutation occurs in body cells, the mutant cells may start to multiply in an uncontrolled way and invade other parts of the body. This is what we know as cancer.

Down's Syndrome is Caused by a Mutation

1) This is a very different type of genetic disorder where a person has three chromosome 21s in their cells.
2) Down's Syndrome is actually an example of a mutation.
3) The problem happens in one of the woman's ovaries. Occasionally both chromosome 21s go into the same egg cell, leaving the other with none. If the egg with two chromosome 21s is fertilised the resulting offspring will have three chromosome 21s.
4) This causes Down's Syndrome. The main effects are: the child will have lower mental ability, and will often be more susceptible to certain diseases.

20   21   22

Mutations play a big part in Natural Selection...

...by creating a new feature with a high survival value. Once upon a time maybe all rabbits had short ears and managed OK. Then one day out popped a mutant with big ears who was always the first to dive for cover. Pretty soon he's got a whole family of them with big ears, all diving for cover before the other rabbits, and before you know it there're only big-eared rabbits left because the rest just didn't hear trouble coming quick enough.

Don't get your genes in a twist, this stuff's easy...

Memorise the headings and learn the numbered points, then cover the page and scribble down everything you can remember. I know it makes your head hurt, but every time you try to remember the stuff, the more it sinks in.

Natural Selection

Darwin's Theory of Natural Selection is Ace

1) This theory is cool and provides a comprehensive explanation for <u>all life on Earth</u>.
2) Mind you, it caused some trouble at the time, because for the first time ever, there was a highly plausible explanation for our own existence, without the need for a "Creator".
3) This was <u>bad news</u> for the religious authorities of the time, who tried to ridicule old Charlie's ideas. But, as they say, "<u>the truth will out</u>".

Darwin made Four Important Observations...

1) All organisms produce <u>more offspring</u> than could possibly survive.
2) But in fact, population numbers tend to remain <u>fairly constant</u> over long periods of time.
3) Organisms in a species show <u>wide variation</u> (due to different genes).
4) <u>Some</u> of the variations are <u>inherited and passed on</u> to the next generation.

...and then made these Two Deductions:

1) Since most offspring don't survive, all organisms must have to <u>struggle for survival</u>.
   (*Being eaten*, *disease* and *competition* cause large numbers of individuals to die).
2) The ones who <u>survive and reproduce</u> will <u>pass on their genes</u>.

This is the famous "<u>Survival of the fittest</u>" statement. Organisms with slightly less survival-value will probably perish first, leaving the <u>strongest</u> and <u>fittest</u> to pass on their <u>genes</u> to the next generation.

Horrible Example 1 — Flat Cockroaches

A recent creepy crawly example of <u>evolution</u> through <u>natural selection</u> is all too apparent in many kitchens around the world.

I knew I should have lost a few pounds...

1) As health inspectors wage war on them, little do they realise how much the <u>cockroach</u> has gone out of its way to fit in.
2) Over the centuries, as man and cockroaches have <u>shared accommodation</u> the cockroaches have actually become <u>smaller and flatter</u> to adapt to our domestic environment.
3) In each generation the smaller, flatter offspring find <u>easier access</u> to our larders and <u>more places to hide</u>, while the <u>larger</u>, <u>bulkier</u> offspring get squashed out.

Scary Example 2: Bacteria Adapt to beat Antibiotics

The "<u>survival of the fittest</u>" affects bacteria just the same as other living things. The trouble is that we're giving them all the help they need to get more and more resistant to our bacterial weapons — antibiotics.

| Someone gets ill | → | Give them antibiotics | → | 99% of the bacteria are killed | → | The person is better, but the bacteria that survive are resistant. | → | If the resistant bacteria get passed on and thrive in someone else, the antibiotics won't help them. |

Overuse of antibiotics is making things worse:
1) Nowadays people <u>expect</u> to get antibiotics for colds and throat infections and stuff.
2) The doctor gives them antibiotics <u>in case</u> it's a bacterial infection.
3) This produces <u>resistant</u> bacteria as shown above.
4) When a resistant bacteria arrives, we have to invent <u>new antibiotics</u> and then the process happens again.
5) Nowadays bacteria are getting resistant at such a rate the development of antibiotics <u>can't keep up</u>. Eeek!

'Natural Selection' — sounds like Vegan Chocolates...

This page is split into three main sections. <u>Memorise</u> the headings, then <u>cover the page</u> and <u>scribble down</u> all you can about each section. Keep trying until you can <u>remember</u> all the important points.

Fossils and Evolution

Fossils are the "remains" of plants and animals which lived millions of years ago.

There are Three ways that Fossils can be Formed:

1) FROM THE hard parts OF ANIMALS   (Most fossils happen this way.)

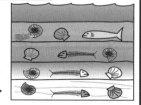

Things like bones, teeth, shells, etc, which don't decay easily, can last a long time when buried. They're eventually replaced by minerals as they decay, forming a rock-like substance shaped like the original hard part. The surrounding sediments also turn to rock, but the fossil stays distinct inside the rock, and eventually someone digs it up.

2) FROM THE softer parts OF ANIMALS OR PLANTS — petrification

buried leaf
replaced by minerals

3) IN PLACES WHERE no decay HAPPENS:

 a) Amber — no oxygen or moisture for the decay microbes.

 b) Glaciers — too cold.

c) Waterlogged bogs — too acidic.

The Theory of Evolution is Cool

1) This suggests that all the animals and plants on Earth gradually "evolved" over millions of years, rather than just suddenly popping into existence. Makes sense.

2) Life on Earth began as simple organisms living in water and gradually everything else evolved from there. And it only took about 4,000,000,000 years.

Fossils Provide Evidence for it

1) Fossils provide lots of evidence for evolution.
2) They show how today's species have changed and developed over millions of years. But there are quite a few "missing links" because the fossil record is incomplete.
3) This is because very very few dead plants or animals actually turn into fossils.
4) Most just decay away completely.

Extinction is Pretty Bad News

The dinosaurs and hairy mammoths became extinct and it's only fossils that tell us they existed at all (notwithstanding the odd questionable glacier story).

> There are three ways a species can become extinct:
> 1) The environment changes too quickly.
> 2) A new predator or disease kills them all.
> 3) They can't compete with another (new) species for food.

As the environment slowly changes, it will gradually favour certain new characteristics amongst the members of the species and over many generations those features will proliferate. In this way, the species constantly adapts to its changing environment. But if the environment changes too fast the whole species may be wiped out — hence extinction...

Don't get bogged down in all this information...

This is pretty interesting stuff, as Science goes. Just make sure you learn every fact, that's all. Dinosaurs never did proper revision and look what happened to them.
(Mind you they did last about 200 million years, which is about 199.9 million more than we have so far...)

Selective Breeding, etc.

In farming, animals and plants are selectively bred to develop the best features, which are basically:

A) <u>Maximum Yield</u> of meat, milk, grain, etc.

B) <u>Good Health</u> and <u>Disease Resistance</u>.

Selective Breeding is Very Simple

<u>Selective breeding</u> is also called <u>artificial selection</u>, because humans artificially select the plants or animals that are going to breed and flourish, according to what <u>we</u> want from them.
This is the basic process involved in selective breeding:

1) From your existing stock select those with the <u>best characteristics</u> and <u>breed them</u> with each other.

2) Select the <u>best</u> of the <u>offspring</u>, and breed them with the best that you already have.

3) Continue this process over several generations to develop the <u>desired traits</u>.

The Main Drawback is a Reduction in the Gene Pool

1) But selective breeding reduces the <u>number of alleles</u> in a population because the farmer keeps breeding from the "best" animals or plants — the same ones all the time.

2) This can cause serious problems if a <u>new disease appears</u>, as all the plants or animals could be wiped out.

3) This is made more likely because all the stock are <u>closely related</u> to each other, so if one of them is going to be killed by a new disease, the others are also likely to succumb to it.

| Selective Breeding | → | Reduction in the number of different alleles (genes) | → | Less chance of any resistant alleles being present in the population | → | Nothing to selectively breed a new strain from |

And now for something completely different...

The Human Genome Project is a Catalogue of our Genes

<u>Genome</u> is one of those fancy Biology words. It means all the genes that a plant or animal has.

1) The <u>Human Genome Project</u> is a complete <u>catalogue</u> of the <u>DNA</u> of every single gene in every chromosome in the human body.

2) In the future, the Human Genome Project may make it possible to <u>screen</u> for <u>genetic diseases</u>, or for genes that make things like heart disease or cancer more likely.

3) There are potential problems though. If <u>genetic information</u> is available to <u>insurance companies</u>, people with <u>genes</u> that make them more likely to suffer from <u>heart disease</u> or <u>cancer</u> might find it very <u>hard</u> to get life insurance. They might ask you about this sort of thing in the Exam.

Don't sit there brooding over it, just learn the info...

<u>Selective breeding is a very simple topic</u>. In the Exam they'll likely give you half a page explaining how a farmer in Sussex did this or that with his crops or cows, and then they'll suddenly ask: "<u>What's meant by selective breeding?</u>" That's when you just write down the three points at the top of this page.

Cloning

Learn this definition of clones:

Clones are genetically identical organisms

Clones occur naturally in both plants and animals. Identical twins are clones of each other.
These days clones are very much a part of the high-tech farming industry.

Embryo Transplants in Cows

Normally, farmers only breed from their best cows and bulls. However, such traditional methods would
only allow the prize cow to produce one new offspring each year. These days the whole process has
been transformed using embryo transplants:

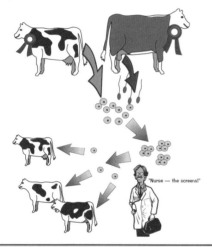

"Nurse — the screens!"

1) Sperm are taken from the prize bull.

2) They're checked for genetic defects and which sex they are.

3) They can also be frozen and used at a later date.

4) Selected prize cows are given hormones to
   make them produce lots of eggs.

5) The cows are then artificially inseminated.

6) The Embryos are taken from the prize cows
   and checked for sex and genetic defects.

7) The embryos are developed and split
   (to form clones) before any cells become specialised.

8) These embryos are implanted into other cows, where
   they grow. They can also be frozen and used at a later date.

Advantages of embryo transplants:
   a) Hundreds of "ideal" offspring can be produced every year from the best bull and cow.
   b) The original prize cow can keep producing prize eggs all year round.
Disadvantages:
   Only the usual drawback with clones — a reduced "gene pool" leading to vulnerability to new diseases.

The Essentials of Commercial Plant Cloning:

Tissue Culture

This is where, instead of starting
with at least a stem and bud, they
just put a few plant cells in a
growth medium with hormones and
it just grows into a new plant. Just
like that! Phew.

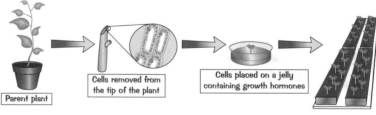

Parent plant

Cells removed from
the tip of the plant

Cells placed on a jelly
containing growth hormones

Hundreds of
clones can be
made from
just one
parent plant

Advantages of tissue culture:

1) Very fast — can produce thousands of plantlets in a few weeks.
2) Very little space needed.
3) Can grow all year — no problem with weather or seasons.
4) New plants are disease-free.
5) New plants can be developed (very quickly) by splicing new genes into plantlets and seeing how they turn out.

Disadvantages of Tissue culture:

Only the usual drawback with clones — a reduced "gene pool" leading to vulnerability to new diseases.

Stop Cloning Around and just learn it...

I hope you realise that they could easily test your knowledge of any sentence on this page. I only put in
stuff you need to know, you know. Practise scribbling out all the facts on this page, mini-essay style.

Genetic Engineering

Genetic Engineering is Ace — hopefully

This is a new science with exciting possibilities, but <u>dangers</u> too. The basic idea is to move sections of genes from one organism to another so that it produces <u>useful biological products</u>. We presently use bacteria to produce <u>human insulin</u> for diabetes sufferers and also to produce <u>human growth hormone</u> for children who aren't growing properly.

Genetic Engineering involves these Important Stages:

1) The useful gene is "<u>cut</u>" from the DNA of, say, a human.
2) <u>The DNA</u> of a <u>bacterium</u> is cut and the human gene is then inserted in its place.
3) The bacterium is <u>cultivated</u> and soon there's <u>millions</u> of similar bacteria producing, e.g., human insulin.
4) This can be done on an <u>industrial scale</u> and the useful product can be <u>separated out</u>.

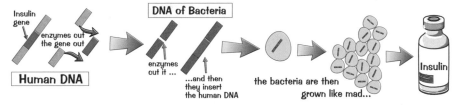

Hence we've turned nasty old bacteria into <u>a useful biological factory</u> — that's modern science for you.

Loads of People think we've Gone Too Far

Science isn't just about cold hard facts any more. There's loads of stuff about whether or not the science is morally right or wrong. No matter what you believe, you've <u>got to learn</u> what the different issues are:

Selective Breeding or Playing God

At the moment selective breeding is allowed in law... so it must be OK? Not everyone thinks so.

1) Some people think it's wrong to <u>manipulate</u> nature to force the evolution of animals for our benefit.
2) Others think it's just what we need to provide <u>nutritious food</u> at a cheap price.
3) There are currently no laws against it — most people see it as <u>normal</u> farming practice.

Cloning — Medical Breakthrough or Moral Headache

1) The biggest issue in cloning at the moment is the cloning of <u>human embryos</u> to get <u>replacement tissues</u> and <u>organs</u> for people who need them.
2) Some countries (including <u>Britain</u> and <u>Japan</u>) have banned human cloning because they think it is <u>morally wrong</u>. People argue that to create a life for spare parts and then kill it is wrong.
3) There's also concern over whether people will use human cloning to produce a child who is an exact copy of the parent. Could help infertile couples, but is morally wrong according to loads of people.

Genetic Engineering or Frankenstein's Monster

1) A big problem for the future of human genetic engineering is the "Designer baby" problem.
2) Changing the genetic make-up of any organisms may affect ecosystems in ways we <u>can't predict</u>.
3) Large seed corporations can make sure they get money every year by selling plants that <u>won't produce fertile seeds</u>, or by producing plants that only respond to <u>their</u> fertilisers.
4) Genetic engineering may also mean that we can produce crops that grow in places they wouldn't before, <u>saving lives</u> in droughts and opening up freezing climates to farming.

Hmmph... Kids these days, they're all the same...

Big stuff, innit...

Revision Summary for Section Two

Gee, all that business about genes and chromosomes and the like — it's all pretty serious stuff, don't you think? It takes a real effort to get your head round it all. There's too many big fancy words, for one thing. But there you go — life's tough and you've just gotta face up to it.
Use these questions to find out what you know — and what you don't. Then look back and learn the bits you don't know. Then try the questions again, and again...

1) What are the two types of variation? Describe their relative importance for plants and animals.

2) List four features of animals which aren't affected at all by environment, and four which are.

3) Name the part of the cell that contains the chromosomes.

4) Give a definition of mitosis. Draw a set of diagrams showing what happens in mitosis.

5) What is asexual reproduction? Give a proper definition for it. How does it involve mitosis?

6) Where does meiosis take place? What kind of cells does meiosis produce?

7) Draw out a sequence of diagrams showing what happens during meiosis.

8) How many pairs of chromosomes are there in a normal human cell nucleus?

9) What happens to the chromosome numbers during meiosis and then during fertilisation?

10) What are X and Y chromosomes to do with? Who has what combination?

11) Draw a genetic inheritance diagram to show how these genes are passed on.

12) What is meant by a monohybrid cross?

13) Give three examples of the wonderful genetics descriptive shorthand.

14) Starting with parental genotypes HH and hh, draw a full genetic inheritance diagram to show the eventual genotypes and phenotypes of the F1 and F2 generations (of hamsters).

15) Briefly describe cystic fibrosis. What causes this disease?
Draw a genetics diagram to show the probability of a child being a sufferer.

16) What causes sickle cell anaemia?

17) Explain the grim odds for Huntington's Chorea.

18) Describe what a mutation is. List the four main causes of mutations.

19) Give an example of harmful and beneficial mutations.

20) Explain how Down's Syndrome is caused.

21) What were Darwin's four observations and two deductions?

22) List the three ways that fossils can form. Describe fully the most common one.

23) Explain how fossils found in rocks support the theory of evolution.

24) Describe the basic procedure in selective breeding (of cows).

25) What is the main drawback of selective breeding in farming?

26) What is the Human Genome Project? Give one good thing and one bad thing about it.

27) Give a good account of embryo transplants.

28) Write down all you know on cloned plants.

29) Briefly describe how genetic engineering works. Give four possible problems with it.

30) What are the ethical issues concerning 'selective breeding' and 'cloning'?

Population Sizes

Four Factors affect the Individual Organisms

These four physical factors fluctuate throughout the day and year. Organisms <u>live</u>, <u>grow</u> and <u>reproduce</u> in places where, and at times when, these conditions are suitable.

> 1) The <u>temperature</u> — this is rarely ideal for any organism.
> 2) The availability of <u>water</u> — vital to all living organisms.
> 3) The <u>amount of light available</u> — very important to plants, but it also affects the visibility for animals.
> 4) <u>Oxygen</u> and <u>carbon dioxide</u> — these affect respiration and photosynthesis.

The Size of any Population depends on Five Factors

1) The <u>total amount of food</u> or nutrients available.
2) The amount of <u>competition</u> there is (from other species) for the same food or nutrients.
3) The amount of <u>light available</u> (this applies only to plants really).
4) The <u>number</u> of <u>predators</u> (or grazers) who may eat the animal (or plant) in question.
5) <u>Disease</u>.

All these factors help to explain why the <u>types</u> of organisms vary from <u>place to place</u> and from <u>time to time</u>.

The dynamics of plant and animal populations are really quite similar:
<u>Plants</u> often compete with each other for <u>space</u>, and for <u>water</u> and <u>nutrients</u> from the soil.
<u>Animals</u> often compete with each other for <u>space</u>, <u>food</u> and <u>water</u>.

Generally organisms will thrive best if:

> 1) There's plenty of the <u>good things</u> in life: food, water, space, shelter, light, etc.
> 2) They're better than the <u>competition</u> at getting it (better *adapted*).
> 3) They don't get <u>eaten</u> (no kidding).
> 4) They don't get <u>ill</u>.

Populations of Prey and Predators go in Cycles

In a community containing prey and predators (as most of them do of course):
1) The <u>population</u> of any species is usually <u>limited</u> by the amount of <u>food</u> available.
2) If the population of the <u>prey</u> increases, then so will the population of the <u>predators</u>.
3) However as the population of predators <u>increases</u>, the number of prey will <u>decrease</u>.

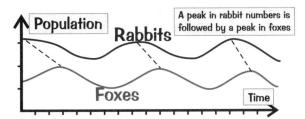

A peak in rabbit numbers is followed by a peak in foxes

i.e. <u>More grass</u> means <u>more rabbits</u>.
More rabbits means <u>more foxes</u>.
But more foxes means <u>less rabbits</u>.
Eventually less rabbits will mean <u>less foxes again</u>.
This <u>up and down pattern</u> continues...

Revision stress — don't let it eat you up...

It's a strange topic is population sizes. In a way it seems like common sense, but it all seems to get so messy. Anyway, <u>learn all the points on this page</u> and you'll be OK with it, I'd think.

Adapt and Survive

If you <u>learn the features</u> that make these animals and plants well adapted, you'll be able to apply them to any other similar creatures they might give you in the Exam.
Chances are you'll get a <u>camel</u>, <u>cactus</u> or <u>polar bear</u> anyway.

The Polar Bear — Designed for Arctic Conditions

The <u>Polar bear</u> has all these features: (which <u>many other Arctic creatures</u> have too, so think on...)

1) <u>Large size</u> and <u>compact shape</u> (i.e. rounded), including dinky little ears, to keep the <u>surface area</u> to a minimum (compared to the body weight) — this all <u>reduces heat loss</u>.

2) A thick layer of <u>blubber</u> for <u>insulation</u> and also to survive hard times when food is scarce.

3) <u>Thick hairy coat</u> for keeping the body heat in.

4) <u>Greasy fur</u> which sheds water after swimming to <u>prevent cooling</u> due to evaporation.

5) <u>White fur</u> to match the surroundings for <u>camouflage</u>.

6) <u>Strong swimmer</u> to catch food in the water and <u>strong runner</u> to run down prey on land.

7) <u>Big feet</u> to <u>spread the weight</u> on snow and ice.

The Camel — Designed for Desert Conditions

The <u>camel</u> has all these features: (most of which are shared by <u>other desert creatures</u>...)

1) It can <u>store</u> a lot of <u>water</u> without problem. It can drink up to <u>20 gallons</u> at once.

2) It loses very little water. There's little <u>urine</u> and very little <u>sweating</u>.

3) It can tolerate <u>big changes</u> in its own <u>body temperature</u> to remove the need for sweating.

4) <u>Large feet</u> to <u>spread load</u> on soft sand.

5) All <u>fat</u> is stored in the <u>hump</u>, there is <u>no layer</u> of body fat. This helps it to <u>lose</u> body heat.

6) <u>Large surface area</u>. The shape of a camel is anything but compact, which gives it more surface area to <u>lose body heat</u> to its surroundings.

7) Its <u>sandy colour</u> gives good <u>camouflage</u>.

The Cactus is also Well Adapted for the Desert

1) It has <u>no leaves</u> — to <u>reduce water loss</u>.

2) It has a <u>small surface area</u> compared to its size which also <u>reduces water loss</u> (1000 x less than normal plants).

3) It <u>stores water</u> in its thick stem.

4) <u>Spines</u> stop herbivores <u>eating</u> them.

5) <u>Shallow</u> but very extensive roots ensure water is <u>absorbed</u> quickly over a large area.

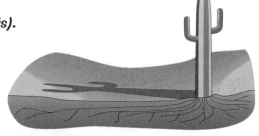

Problems Caused By Farming

Farming Produces a Lot of Food, Which is Great but...

1) Farming is important to us because it allows us to produce _a lot of food_ from _less and less land_.
2) These days it has become quite a _high-tech_ industry. Food production is _big business_.
3) The great advantage of this is a _huge variety_ of _top quality_ foods, _all year round_, at _cheap prices_.
4) This is a far cry from Britain _50 years ago_ when food had to be _rationed_ by the government because there simply _wasn't enough_ for everyone. That's hard to imagine today... but try...

Pesticides Disturb Food Chains

1) Pesticides are sprayed onto most crops to kill the various insects that can damage the crops.
2) Unfortunately, they also kill lots of harmless insects such as bees and beetles.
3) This can cause a shortage of food for many insect-eating birds.
4) Pesticides tend to be poisonous and there's always the danger of the poison passing on to other animals (as well as humans).

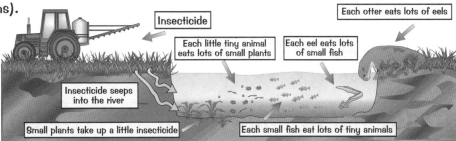

This is well illustrated by the case of otters which were almost wiped out over much of crop-dominated Southern England by a pesticide called DDT in the early 1960s. The diagram shows the food chain which ends with the otter. DDT is not excreted so it accumulates along the food chain and the otter ends up with all the DDT collected by all the other animals.

Fertilisers Damage Lakes and Rivers — Eutrophication

1) _Fertilisers_ which contain _nitrates_ are essential to _modern farming_.
2) Without them crops wouldn't grow nearly so well, and _food yields_ would be _well down_.
3) This is because the crops take _nitrates_ out of the soil and these nitrates need to be _replaced_.
4) The _problems_ start if some of the _rich fertiliser_ finds its way into _rivers_ and _streams_.
5) This happens quite easily if _too much fertiliser_ is applied, especially if it rains soon afterwards.
6) The result is _EUTROPHICATION_, which basically means "_too much of a good thing_".
   (_Raw sewage_ pumped into rivers also causes _EUTROPHICATION_ by providing food for microbes.)

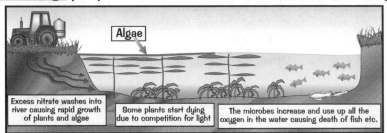

As the picture shows, _too many nitrates_ in the water cause a sequence of "_mega-growth_", "_mega-death_" and "_mega-decay_" involving most of the _plant_ and _animal life_ in the water.

7) _Farmers_ need to take _a lot more care_ when spreading _artificial fertilisers_.

"There's nowt wrong wi' just spreadin' muck on it..."

Make sure you distinguish between _pesticides_ (which kill bugs) and _fertilisers_ (which supply nutrients to the plants). They can both cause harm but for totally different reasons. You have to learn the details carefully. _Mini-essay_ time again I'd say. _Cover the page and scribble_...

Managed Ecosystems

A Salmon Fish Farm Ecosystem in Bonny Scotland

Problem: <u>Fish</u> is becoming an <u>increasingly popular</u> dish, but fish stocks are dwindling.
Solution: "<u>Fish farms</u>" were set up to deliberately rear fish in a controlled way.

Salmon <u>fish farming</u> on the West Coast of Scotland is the best example:

1) The fish are kept in <u>cages</u> in a <u>sea loch</u>, to <u>protect</u> them from <u>predators</u> and also to <u>reduce</u> their energy usage due to swimming about looking for food.

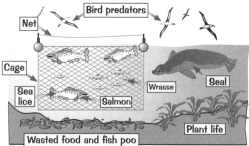

2) They're fed a carefully <u>controlled diet</u> of food pellets, to avoid <u>pollution</u> to the loch. <u>Excess</u> food and faeces from the salmon could cause <u>too many bacteria</u> using up the <u>oxygen</u>, so <u>animals</u> wouldn't survive at the <u>bottom</u> of the loch.

3) The <u>eggs</u> are <u>artificially fertilised</u> and the young are reared in special tanks to remove any risk from <u>predators</u> and ensure as many survive as possible.

4) Fish kept in nets are more prone to <u>disease</u> and <u>parasites</u>. One pest is <u>fish lice</u> and they can be treated with a <u>chemical</u> called <u>Dichlorvos</u> which kills them.

5) However, because <u>chemical pesticides</u> tend to <u>linger</u> in the loch and harm other creatures, <u>biological pest control</u> is used if possible. E.g. using a small fish called the <u>wrasse</u> to eat the fish lice.

Traditional Farming is still perfectly Viable

Modern farming produces a lot of <u>top quality</u> food and we all appreciate it on the supermarket shelves. However, you certainly could <u>not</u> describe modern farming as "<u>a carefully managed ecosystem</u>" and each new modern farming technique tends to create various "<u>unforeseen</u>" or "<u>unfore-cared-about</u>" consequences.

<u>Traditional</u> farming methods do still work (amazingly!), but they produce <u>less</u> food per acre and it's more <u>expensive</u> too. The positive side is that the <u>whole ecosystem</u> stays in <u>balance</u>, the countryside still looks pretty *plus* the animals get a <u>fair deal</u>. Europe is now <u>over-producing food</u> in a big way — it may be time to pay more attention to these things rather than "<u>maximum food yield at all costs</u>". It <u>is</u> possible to produce plenty of food *and* maintain a balanced ecosystem. The <u>three main things</u> that can be done are:

1) Use of <u>organic fertilisers</u> (i.e. spreading muck on it — and there's nowt wrong wi' that).
2) <u>Reforestation</u> and "<u>set-aside</u>" land for meadows, to give <u>wild plants and animals</u> a chance.
3) <u>Biological control</u> of pests. Controlling pests by getting <u>other creatures</u> to eat them is a reasonable alternative to <u>pesticides</u>. It may not always be as effective, but there are <u>no harmful food chain problems</u>.

Conserving Endangered Species and their Habitats

Kill, kill, kill, oops they're all <u>dead</u>. Chop, chop, chop, oops they're <u>homeless</u>... and <u>dead</u>.
We kill species of plants and animals in <u>two</u> ways: 1) <u>Directly</u> for food, sport, fur coats, pest control, etc.
                                                   2) By destroying their <u>habitats</u>.
If done in a controlled way, animal and plant populations will remain at a sustainable level.
If done in an <u>uncontrolled</u> way, species will become endangered and (if nothing is done) <u>extinct</u>.

E.g. 1 — Barn Owls are endangered because:
• we're destroying their habitat (hedgerows, barns, meadows)
• we're poisoning their food (voles and mice) with pesticides

E.g. 2 — North Atlantic Cod are endangered because:
• we're eating them all
• we're eating their kids too

Och aye the noo, wee laddie — just learn the fa'acts...

Make sure you can describe a "<u>balanced ecosystem</u>" and a "<u>carefully managed ecosystem</u>", with examples. And be sure you know why organic farming creates a balanced ecosystem and why modern farming doesn't. Then leave your cod with barn owl sauce and learn the endangered species examples.

There's Too Many People

There's one born every minute — and it's too many

1) The <u>population</u> of the world is currently <u>rising out of control</u>, as the graph shows.

2) This is mostly due to <u>modern medicine</u> which has stopped widespread death from <u>disease</u>.

3) It's also due to modern farming methods which can now provide the <u>food</u> needed for so many hungry mouths.

4) The <u>death rate</u> is now <u>much lower</u> than the <u>birth rate</u> in many under-developed countries.
   In other words there are <u>lots more babies born</u> than people <u>dying</u>.

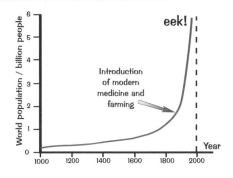

5) This creates <u>big problems</u> for those countries trying to cope with all those extra people.

6) Even providing <u>basic health care</u> and <u>education</u> (e.g. about contraception) is difficult, never mind finding them <u>places to live</u>, and <u>food to eat</u>.

Improving living Standards Adds Even More Pressure

The rapidly increasing population is not the only pressure on the environment.
The <u>increasing standard of living</u> in all <u>countries</u> also demands more from the environment.
These <u>two</u> factors mean that:

1) Raw materials, including <u>non-renewable</u> energy resources, are rapidly being used up.

2) More and more <u>waste</u> is being produced.

3) Unless waste is properly handled <u>more pollution</u> will be caused.

When the Earth's population was much smaller, the effects of human activity were usually small and local.

More People Means Less Land for Plants and Animals

There are <u>four</u> main ways that humans <u>reduce</u> the amount of land available for other <u>animals</u> and <u>plants</u>.

1) <u>Building</u>

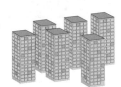

2) <u>Farming</u>

3) <u>Dumping Waste</u>

4) <u>Quarrying</u>

More People Means More Environmental Damage

Human activity can pollute all three parts of the environment:

1) <u>Water</u> – with sewage, fertiliser and toxic chemicals.

2) <u>Air</u> – with smoke and gases such as sulphur dioxide.

3) <u>Land</u> – with toxic chemicals, such as pesticides and herbicides.
   These may then be washed from the land into water.

Learn the facts first — then you can build your rocket...

It's real scary innit — the way that graph of world population seems to be pointing nearly vertically upwards... tricky. Anyway, you just worry about your Exams instead, and make sure you learn all the grim facts. Four sections — <u>mini-essays</u> for each, <u>till you know it all</u>.

Section Three — Environment

Atmospheric Pollution

The Three Main Sources of Atmospheric Pollution are...

1) Burning fossil fuels

1) Fossil fuels are coal, oil and natural gas.
2) The main culprits who burn these are cars and power stations.
3) They release mostly carbon dioxide, which adds to the greenhouse effect.
4) But they also release sulphur dioxide and oxides of nitrogen, which are causing acid rain.

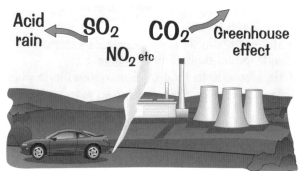

Acid rain ← SO_2 CO_2 → Greenhouse effect
NO_2 etc

2) CFC's (Chloro-fluoro-carbons)

1) These are used in aerosols, fridges, air-conditioning units and polystyrene foam.
2) They are a major cause of a hole in the ozone layer.
3) This allows harmful UV rays to reach the Earth's surface.

3) Lead used in Petrol

1) "Old-fashioned" leaded (4 star) petrol contained lead which pollutes the air.
2) The lead is breathed in and causes damage to the nervous system.

People are usually OK at remembering the three sources of pollution in the atmosphere, but when it comes to sorting out their effects, it's a whole different ball game. You have to make a real effort to learn exactly where each type of pollution comes from and exactly what the effect of each pollutant is. There are dozens of ways to get them all mixed up, but there are no marks for being a clot.

Deforestation increases CO_2 and the Greenhouse Effect

We have already pretty well deforested our country. Now many under-developed tropical countries are doing the same for timber and to provide land for agriculture. If the loss of millions of species wasn't enough this also causes a major increase in the greenhouse gas carbon dioxide (CO_2). Deforestation increases CO_2 in the atmosphere in two ways:

1) The trees unsuitable for timber are burned, releasing CO_2 directly into the atmosphere. Microbes also release CO_2 by decaying the felled trees that remain.

2) Because living trees use CO_2 for photosynthesis, removing these trees means less CO_2 is removed from the atmosphere.

Revision and Pollution — the two bugbears of modern life...

You must make a real effort to sort out the different types of air pollution. Notice for example that cars give out three different things which cause three different problems. Learn it good.

The Greenhouse Effect

Carbon Dioxide and Methane Trap Heat from the Sun

1) The <u>temperature</u> of the Earth is a <u>balance</u> between the heat it gets from the Sun and the heat it radiates back out into space.

2) The <u>atmosphere</u> acts like an <u>insulating layer</u> and keeps some of the heat <u>in</u>.

3) This is exactly what happens in a <u>greenhouse</u> or a <u>conservatory</u>.

   The sun shines <u>into it</u> and the glass keeps the <u>heat in</u> so it just gets <u>hotter</u> and <u>hotter</u>.

Light energy from the Sun

Layer of CO₂ and Methane

Heat radiation reflected back to Earth

4) There are several different gases in the atmosphere which are very good at keeping the <u>heat in</u>. They are called "<u>greenhouse gases</u>", oddly enough. The <u>main ones</u> that we worry about are <u>methane</u> and <u>carbon dioxide</u>, because the levels of these are rising quite sharply.

5) Human activity is increasing the <u>Greenhouse Effect</u>, causing the Earth to <u>warm up</u> very slowly.

The Greenhouse Effect may cause Flooding and Drought....(!)

1) Changes in weather patterns and climate could cause problems of <u>drought</u> or <u>flooding</u>.

2) The <u>melting</u> of the polar ice caps would <u>raise sea levels</u> and could cause <u>flooding</u> to many <u>low-lying coastal parts</u> of the world including many <u>major cities</u>.

Modern Industrial Life is Increasing the Greenhouse Effect

1) The level of <u>CO₂</u> in the atmosphere used to be nicely <u>balanced</u> between the CO₂ released by <u>respiration</u> (of animals and plants) and the CO₂ absorbed by <u>photosynthesis</u>.

2) However, mankind has been burning <u>massive amounts</u> of <u>fossil fuels</u> in the last two hundred years or so.

3) We have also been <u>cutting down trees</u> all over the world to make space for living and farming. This is called <u>deforestation</u>.

4) The level of CO₂ in the atmosphere has <u>gone up</u> by about <u>20%</u>, and will <u>continue to rise</u> ever more steeply as long as we keep <u>burning fossil fuels</u> — just look at that graph — eek!

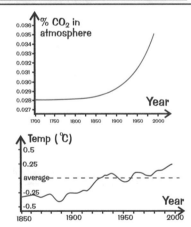

% CO₂ in atmosphere

Year

Temp (°C)

average

Year

Methane is Also a Problem

1) <u>Methane gas</u> is also contributing to the <u>Greenhouse Effect</u>.

2) It's produced <u>naturally</u> from various sources, such as <u>natural marshland</u>.

3) However, the two sources of methane which are <u>on the increase</u> are:
   a) <u>Rice growing</u>
   b) <u>Cattle rearing</u> — it's the cows "pumping" that's the problem, believe it or not.

Learn the facts first — then start building your ark...

I bet you never realised there were so many drivelly details on the Greenhouse Effect.
Well there <u>are</u> and I'm afraid they could all come up in your Exam, so you just gotta learn them.
Use the good old <u>mini-essay</u> method for each section, and <u>scribble down what you know</u>...

Acid Rain

Burning Fossil Fuels Causes Acid Rain

1) When fossil fuels are burned they release mostly <u>carbon dioxide</u>, which is increasing the <u>Greenhouse Effect</u>. They also release <u>two</u> other harmful gases:
    a) <u>sulphur dioxide</u>   b) various <u>nitrogen oxides</u>.
2) When these mix with clouds they form <u>acids</u>. This then falls as <u>acid rain</u>.
3) <u>Cars</u> and <u>power stations</u> are the main causes of acid rain.

Acid Rain Kills Fish, Trees and Statues

1) Acid rain causes lakes to become acidic, which has a <u>severe effect</u> on its <u>ecosystem</u>.
2) The way this happens is that the acid causes <u>aluminium salts</u> (in the soil) to <u>dissolve</u> into the water. The resulting <u>aluminium ions</u> are <u>poisonous</u> to many fish and birds.
3) Acid rain kills <u>trees</u>.
4) Acid rain damages <u>limestone buildings</u> and ruins stone statues.

Acid Rain is Prevented by Cleaning up Emissions

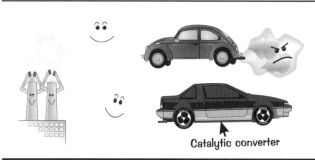

Catalytic converter

1) <u>Power stations</u> now have <u>Acid Gas Scrubbers</u> to take the harmful gases <u>out</u> before they release their fumes into the atmosphere.
2) <u>Cars</u> are now being fitted with <u>catalytic converters</u> to clean up their <u>exhaust gases</u>.
3) The other way of reducing acid rain is simply to <u>reduce</u> our usage of <u>fossil fuels</u>.

Learn about Acid Rain — and always take a coat...

There aren't too many details on acid rain. If you can't learn all this lot properly then you're just not trying. Don't forget they won't ask you easy stuff like "Is acid rain caused by cars or monkeys?", they'll test you on trickier stuff like "Which gases cause acid rain and why?". <u>Learn and enjoy</u>. And <u>smile</u>.

Revision Summary for Section Three

There's a lot of words in Section Three. Most topics are pretty waffly with a lot of drivelly facts, and it can be real hard to learn them all. But learn them you must. You need to practise scribbling down what you can remember on each topic, and then checking back to see what you missed. These questions give you a pretty good idea of what you should know. You need to practise and practise them — till you can float through them all, like a cloud or something.

1) What are the *four* basic things which determine the size of a population of a species?

2) Sketch a graph of prey and predator populations and explain the shapes.

3) List seven survival features of the polar bear and of the camel.

4) Give five survival features for the cactus.

5) Explain in detail how pesticides enter the food chain. What happened with DDT in the '60s?

6) What happens when too much nitrate fertiliser is put onto fields? Give full details.

7) What is the big fancy name given to this problem? How can it be avoided?

8) Describe the details of salmon fish farms in Scotland.

9) Explain why organic farming produces a balanced ecosystem and modern farming doesn't.

10) Why are chemical pesticides used? What are the drawbacks of doing this?

11) Give two examples of endangered species and say why each one is dying out.

12) What is happening to the world population? What is largely responsible for this trend?

13) What can be said about the birth rate and death rate in many developing countries?

14) What problems does a rapidly increasing population create for a country?

15) What effect does more and more people have on the environment?

16) What are the three main sources of atmospheric pollution?

17) What are the precise environmental effects of each of these three sources of pollution?

18) What does CFC stand for? Where do CFCs come from? What damage do they do?

19) List two problems resulting from deforestation in tropical countries. Why do they do it?

20) What are the two main gases which are increasing the Greenhouse Effect?

21) Explain how the Greenhouse Effect happens. What dire consequences could there be?

22) What is causing the rise in levels of each of the two problem gases? What is the solution?

23) Which gases cause acid rain? Where do these gases come from?

24) Give three harmful effects of acid rain. Explain exactly how fish are killed.

25) Give three ways that acid rain can be reduced.

Section Three — Environment

Atoms

The structure of atoms is real simple. I mean, gee, there's nothing to them. Just learn and enjoy.

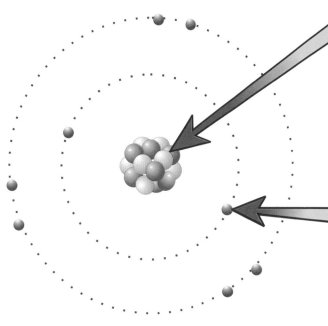

The Nucleus

1) It's in the <u>middle</u> of the atom.
2) It contains <u>protons</u> and <u>neutrons</u>.
3) It has a <u>positive charge</u> because of the protons.
4) Almost the <u>whole mass</u> of the atom is <u>concentrated</u> in the <u>nucleus</u>.
5) But size-wise it's <u>tiny</u> compared to the atom as a whole.

The Electrons

1) Move <u>around</u> the nucleus.
2) They're <u>negatively charged</u>.
3) They're <u>tiny</u>, but they cover a <u>lot of space</u>.
4) The <u>volume</u> of their orbits determines <u>how big</u> the atom is.
5) They have <u>virtually no mass</u>.
6) They occupy <u>shells</u> around the nucleus.
7) These shells explain the <u>whole of Chemistry</u>.

Atoms are <u>real tiny</u>, don't forget.
They're <u>too small to see</u>, even with a microscope.

Number of Protons Equals Number of Electrons

1) Neutral atoms have <u>no charge</u> overall.
2) The <u>charge</u> on the <u>electrons</u> is the <u>same</u> size as the charge on the <u>protons</u> but <u>opposite</u>.
3) This means the <u>number of protons</u> always <u>equals</u> the <u>number of electrons</u> in a <u>neutral atom</u>.
4) If some electrons are <u>added</u> or <u>removed</u>, the atom becomes <u>charged</u> and is then an <u>ion</u>.
5) The number of neutrons isn't fixed but is usually <u>just a bit higher</u> than the number of protons.

Know Your Particles

<u>Protons</u> are <u>Heavy</u> and <u>Positively Charged</u>
<u>Neutrons</u> are <u>Heavy</u> and <u>Neutral</u>
<u>Electrons</u> are <u>Tiny</u> and <u>Negatively Charged</u>

PARTICLE	MASS	CHARGE
Proton	1	+1
Neutron	1	0
Electron	$\frac{1}{2000}$	- 1

Basic Atom facts — they don't take up much space...

This stuff on atoms should be permanently engraved in the minds of everyone.
I don't understand how people can get through the day without knowing this stuff, really I don't.
<u>Learn it now</u>, and watch as the Universe unfolds and reveals its timeless mysteries to you...

Atoms

Atomic Number and Mass Number

Come on. These are just <u>two simple numbers</u> for goodness' sake.
It just can't be that difficult to remember what they tell you about an atom.

The Mass Number
— Total of Protons and Neutrons

The atomic Number
— Number of Protons

$$^{23}_{11}\text{Na}$$

<u>Points to Note</u>
1) The <u>atomic number</u> tells you how many <u>protons</u> there are.
2) This <u>also</u> tells you how many <u>electrons</u> there are.
3) To get the number of <u>neutrons</u> — just <u>subtract</u> the <u>atomic number</u> from the <u>mass number</u>.
4) The <u>mass number</u> is always the <u>biggest</u> number. It tells you the relative mass of the atom.
5) The <u>mass</u> number is always <u>roughly double</u> the <u>atomic</u> number.
6) Which means there's about the <u>same</u> number of protons as neutrons in any nucleus.

Isotopes are the same except for an extra neutron or two

A favourite trick Exam question: "<u>Explain what is meant by the term Isotope</u>"
The trick is that it's impossible to explain what one isotope is.
You have to outsmart them and always start your answer *"ISOTOPES ARE..."*
<u>LEARN the definition</u>:

> Isotopes are: <u>different atomic forms</u> of the <u>same element</u>, which have
> the <u>SAME</u> number of <u>PROTONS</u> but a <u>DIFFERENT</u> number of <u>NEUTRONS</u>.

1) The upshot is: isotopes must have the <u>same atomic number</u> but <u>different mass numbers</u>.
2) <u>If</u> they had <u>different</u> atomic numbers, they'd be <u>different elements altogether</u>.
3) A very popular pair of isotopes are <u>carbon-12</u> and <u>carbon-14</u>.

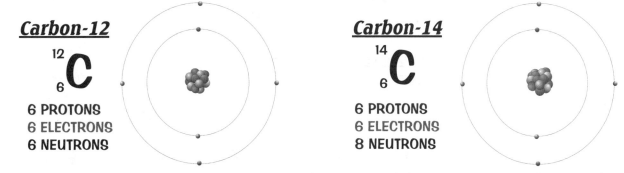

Carbon-12

$$^{12}_{6}\text{C}$$

6 PROTONS
6 ELECTRONS
6 NEUTRONS

Carbon-14

$$^{14}_{6}\text{C}$$

6 PROTONS
6 ELECTRONS
8 NEUTRONS

<u>The number of electrons decides the chemistry of the element</u>. If the <u>atomic number</u> is the same, then
the <u>number of protons</u> is the same, so the <u>number of electrons</u> is the same, so the <u>chemistry</u> is the same.
<u>The different number of neutrons in the nucleus doesn't affect the chemical behaviour at all</u>.

Learn what those blinking numbers mean...

There really isn't that much information on this page — three definitions, a couple of diagrams
and a dozen or so extra details.   All you gotta do is <u>read it</u>, <u>learn it</u>, <u>cover the page</u> and <u>scribble
it all down again</u>. Smile and enjoy.

Electron Shells and Ionic Bonding

The fact that electrons occupy "shells" around the nucleus is what causes the whole of chemistry. Remember that, and watch how it applies to each bit of it. It's ace.

Electron Shell Rules:

1) Electrons always occupy <u>shells</u> or <u>energy levels</u>.

2) The <u>lowest</u> energy levels are <u>always filled first</u>.

3) Only <u>a certain number</u> of electrons are allowed in each shell:
<u>1st shell</u>: 2   <u>2nd Shell</u>: 8   <u>3rd Shell</u>: 8

4) Atoms are much <u>happier</u> when they have <u>full electron shells</u>.

5) In most atoms the <u>outer shell</u> is <u>not full</u> and this makes the atom want to <u>react</u>.

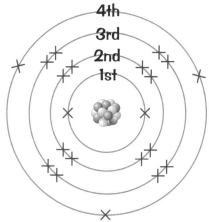

4th shell still filling

Ionic Bonding — Swapping Electrons

In <u>ionic bonding</u>, atoms <u>lose or gain electrons</u> to form <u>charged particles</u> (ions) which are then <u>strongly attracted</u> to one another, (because of the attraction of opposite charges, + and –).

A shell with just one electron is well keen to get rid...

<u>All</u> the atoms over at the <u>left hand side</u> of the periodic table, such as <u>sodium, potassium, calcium</u> etc. have just <u>one or two electrons</u> in their outer shell. And basically they're <u>pretty keen to get shot of them</u>, because then they'll only have <u>full shells</u> left, which is how they <u>like</u> it.
So given half a chance they do get rid, and that leaves the atom as an <u>ion</u> instead.
Now ions aren't the kind of things that sit around quietly watching the world go by.
They tend to <u>leap</u> at the first passing ion with an <u>opposite charge</u> and stick to it like glue.

A nearly full shell is well keen to get that extra electron...

On the <u>other side</u> of the periodic table, the elements in <u>Group Six</u> and <u>Group Seven</u>, such as <u>oxygen</u> and <u>chlorine</u>, have outer shells which are <u>nearly full</u>. They're obviously pretty keen to <u>gain</u> that <u>extra one or two electrons</u> to fill the shell up. When they do of course they become <u>ions</u>, you know, not the kind of things to sit around, and before you know it, <u>pop</u>, they've latched onto the atom (ion) that gave up the electron a moment earlier. The reaction of sodium and chlorine is a <u>classic case</u>:

The <u>chlorine</u> atom <u>picks up</u> the <u>spare electron</u> and becomes a Cl⁻ ion.

The <u>sodium</u> atom <u>gives up</u> its <u>outer electron</u> and becomes an Na⁺ ion.

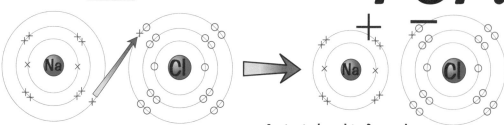

POP!

An <u>ionic bond</u> is formed

Full Shells — it's the name of the game, pal...

There's quite a lot of words on this page but only to hammer home three very basic points:
1) Electrons have shells — with rules   2) Ionic bonds involve swapping electrons
3) Some atoms like to lose them, some like to gain them.   <u>Learn all the highlighted bits.</u>

Common Tests and Hazard Symbols

You need to know these <u>six easy lab tests</u>:

1) <u>Chlorine bleaches damp litmus paper</u>

(i.e. it <u>turns it white</u>).

2) <u>Oxygen relights a glowing splint</u>

The standard test for <u>oxygen</u> is that it <u>relights a glowing splint</u>.

3) <u>Carbon dioxide turns limewater milky</u>

<u>Carbon dioxide</u> can be detected by <u>turning limewater cloudy</u> when it's bubbled through.

4) <u>The three lab tests for Water</u>

Water can be detected in three ways:
a) by its <u>boiling point</u> of <u>100°C</u>
b) by turning <u>white anhydrous copper sulphate</u> to <u>blue hydrated copper sulphate</u> (and getting hot)
c) by turning <u>anhydrous cobalt chloride paper</u> from <u>blue</u> to <u>pink</u>.

5) <u>Lab test for Hydrogen — the notorious "Squeaky pop"</u>

Just bring a <u>lighted splint</u> near the gas with air around.
If it's hydrogen it'll make a "<u>squeaky pop</u>" as it burns with the oxygen in the air to form H_2O.

You need to know the test for alkenes as well — see page 51.

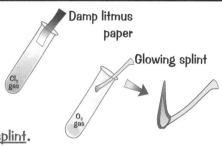
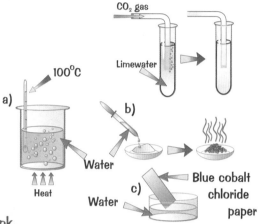

Hazard Symbols

The official hazard symbol for "harmful" and "irritant" is a black cross. Some products add an "h" or "i" to show the difference.

Oxidising
<u>Provides oxygen</u> which allows other materials to <u>burn more fiercely</u>.
<u>Example:</u> Liquid Oxygen.

Highly Flammable
<u>Catches fire</u> easily.
<u>Example:</u> Petrol.

Toxic
<u>Can cause death</u> either by swallowing, breathing in, or absorption through the skin. <u>Example:</u> Cyanide.

Harmful
Similar to toxic but <u>not quite as dangerous</u>.
<u>Example:</u> Petrol, meths.

Irritant
Not corrosive but <u>can cause reddening or blistering of the skin</u>.
<u>Examples:</u> Bleach, children, etc.

Corrosive
<u>Attacks and destroys living tissues</u>, including eyes and skin.
<u>Example:</u> Sulphuric acid.

Learn the Six Lab Tests — easy as squeaky pop...

This is pretty basic stuff, but people still lose marks in the Exam because they don't make sure to learn all the little details really thoroughly. That's true for just about everything in this book. It's no good just letting your eyes drift lazily across the page and thinking "Oh yeah, I know all that stuff". You've gotta really make sure you <u>do</u> know it all. <u>And there's only one way to do that</u> — so do it now.

Section Four — Earth Chemistry

Fractional Distillation of Crude Oil

1) <u>Crude oil</u> is formed from the buried remains of plants and animals — it's a fossil fuel. Over millions of years, with high temperature and pressure, the remains turn to crude oil which can be drilled up.
2) Crude oil is a <u>mixture</u> of <u>hydrocarbons</u> of different sized molecules.
3) <u>Hydrocarbons</u> are basically <u>fuels</u> such as petrol and diesel. They're made of just carbon and hydrogen.
4) The <u>bigger</u> and <u>longer</u> the molecules, the <u>less runny</u> the hydrocarbon (fuel) is.
5) <u>Fractional distillation</u> splits crude oil up into its separate <u>fractions</u>.
6) The <u>shorter</u> the molecules, the <u>lower</u> the <u>temperature</u> at which that fraction <u>condenses</u>.

Crude Oil is Split into Separate Hydrocarbons (fuels)

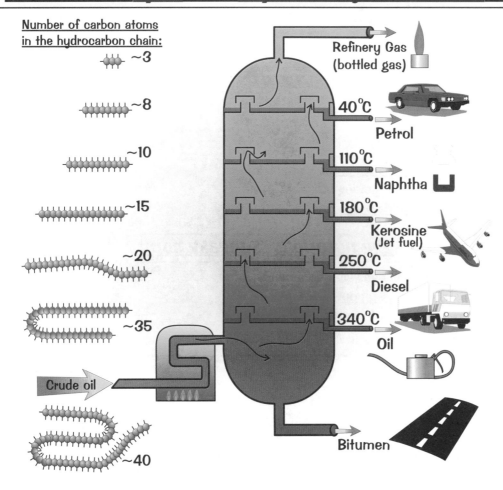

Number of carbon atoms in the hydrocarbon chain:

~3

~8

~10

~15

~20

~35

Crude oil

~40

Refinery Gas (bottled gas)

40°C — Petrol

110°C — Naphtha

180°C — Kerosine (Jet fuel)

250°C — Diesel

340°C — Oil

Bitumen

The <u>fractionating column</u> works <u>continuously</u>, with heated crude oil piped in at the <u>bottom</u> and the various <u>fractions</u> being <u>constantly tapped off</u> at the different levels where they <u>condense</u>.

Crude oil is a very big part of modern life

1) There's a <u>massive industry</u> with scientists working to find oil reserves, take it out of the ground, and turn it into useful products.
2) It provides the <u>fuel</u> for most modern transport.
3) It also provides the <u>raw materials</u> for making various <u>chemicals</u> including <u>plastics</u>. Plastics are just ace, of course. The world without plastics? Why, it would be the end of civilisation as we know it...
4) Oil can be serious bad news for the <u>environment</u>. Oil slicks at sea, old engine oil down the drain, plastics that won't rot if you throw them away... <u>Some</u> things can be <u>recycled</u> though, which helps.

Revising for oil — you know the drill...

A typical question would show a fractionating column and ask you which bit you'd expect petrol or diesel to come out of, or ask you how long the carbon chain of diesel is, or ask you to give the main uses of crude oil. So make sure you know <u>all</u> the details. When you think you do, <u>cover up the page</u> and <u>scribble down</u> all the details including the diagram. <u>Then try again.</u>

Using Hydrocarbons

Hydrocarbons are long chain molecules

As the <u>size</u> of the hydrocarbon molecule <u>increases</u>:

1) The <u>boiling point</u> increases

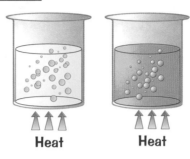

2) It gets <u>less flammable</u>
   (doesn't set fire so easy)

Heat   Heat

3) It gets <u>more viscous</u>
   (doesn't flow so easy)

4) It gets <u>less volatile</u>

The <u>vapours</u> of the more <u>volatile</u> hydrocarbons are <u>very flammable</u> and pose a serious <u>fire risk</u>.
So don't smoke at the petrol station. (In fact, don't smoke at all, it's stupid.)

Complete combustion of Hydrocarbons is safe

The <u>complete combustion</u> of any hydrocarbon in oxygen will produce only
<u>carbon dioxide</u> and <u>water</u> as waste products, which are both quite <u>clean</u> and <u>non poisonous</u>.

hydrocarbon + oxygen → carbon dioxide + water (+ energy)

Many <u>gas room heaters</u> release these <u>waste gases</u> into the room, which is perfectly OK.
As long as the gas heater is working properly and the room is well ventilated there's
no problem. When there's <u>plenty of oxygen</u> the gas burns with a <u>clean blue flame</u>.

But Incomplete combustion of Hydrocarbons is NOT safe

If there <u>isn't enough oxygen</u> the combustion will be <u>incomplete</u>.
This gives <u>carbon monoxide</u> and <u>carbon</u> as waste products,
and produces a <u>smoky yellow flame</u>:

hydrocarbon + oxygen → CO_2 + H_2O + carbon monoxide + carbon (+ energy)

The <u>carbon monoxide</u> is a <u>colourless</u>, <u>odourless</u> and <u>poisonous</u> gas and it's <u>very dangerous</u>.
Every year people are <u>killed</u> while they sleep due to <u>faulty</u> gas fires and boilers filling the room
with <u>deadly carbon monoxide</u>, CO, and nobody realising.
The black carbon given off produces <u>sooty marks</u> and is a <u>clue</u> that the fuel is <u>not</u> burning fully.

The one burning question is... have you learnt it all...

Four features of hydrocarbons which change with increasing chain length, and the details for
complete and incomplete combustion. <u>All worth juicy marks in the Exam</u>. So learn and enjoy.

Cracking Hydrocarbons

Cracking — splitting up long chain hydrocarbons

1) <u>Long chain hydrocarbons</u> form <u>thick gloopy liquids</u> like <u>tar</u> which aren't all that useful.
2) The process called <u>cracking</u> turns them into <u>shorter molecules</u> which are much more <u>useful</u>.

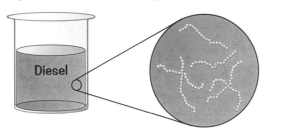

3) <u>Cracking</u> is a form of <u>thermal decomposition</u>, which just means <u>breaking</u> molecules down into <u>simpler</u> molecules by <u>heating</u> them.
4) A lot of the longer molecules produced from <u>fractional distillation</u> are <u>cracked</u> into smaller ones because there's <u>more demand</u> for products like <u>petrol</u> and <u>paraffin</u> (jet fuel) than for diesel or lubricating oil.
5) More importantly, cracking produces <u>extra alkenes</u> which are needed for <u>making plastics</u>.

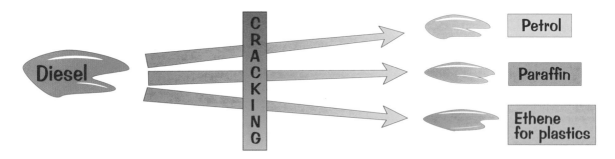

Industrial Conditions for Cracking: hot, plus a catalyst

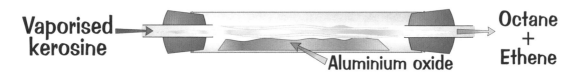

Vaporised kerosine → Aluminium oxide → Octane + Ethene

1) <u>Vaporised hydrocarbons</u> are passed over <u>powdered catalyst</u> at about <u>400°C – 700°C</u>.
2) <u>Aluminium oxide</u> is the catalyst used.
   The <u>long chain</u> molecules <u>split apart</u> or "crack" on the <u>surface</u> of the bits of catalyst.

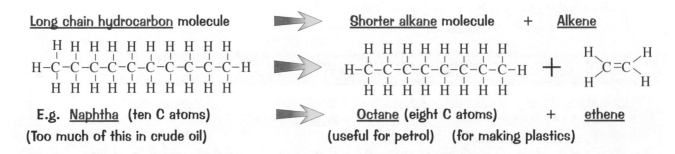

E.g. <u>Naphtha</u> (ten C atoms)   <u>Octane</u> (eight C atoms)   +   <u>ethene</u>
(Too much of this in crude oil)   (useful for petrol)   (for making plastics)

Chemistry — what a cracking subject it is...

Five details about the whys and wherefores, two details of the industrial conditions and a specific example showing typical products: a shorter chain alkane and an alkene. <u>LEARN IT ALL</u>.

Alkanes and Alkenes

Crude oil contains both <u>alkanes</u> and <u>alkenes</u>. You have to know the differences between them.

ALKANES have all C–C SINGLE bonds

1) They're made up of <u>chains</u> of carbon atoms with <u>single covalent bonds</u> between them.
2) They're called <u>saturated hydrocarbons</u> because they have <u>no spare bonds</u> left.
3) This is also why they <u>don't</u> decolourise <u>bromine water</u> — no spare bonds.
4) They <u>won't</u> form <u>polymers</u> — same reason again, <u>no spare bonds</u>.
5) The first four alkanes are <u>methane</u> (natural gas), <u>ethane</u>, <u>propane</u> and <u>butane</u>.
6) They <u>burn cleanly</u> producing <u>carbon dioxide</u> and <u>water</u>.

Bromine water
+ alkane
— still brown.

1) Methane
Formula: CH_4

(natural gas)

2) Ethane
Formula: C_2H_6

3) Propane
Formula: C_3H_8

4) Butane
Formula: C_4H_{10}

ALKENES have a C=C DOUBLE bond

Bromine water
+ alkene —
decolourised

1) They're <u>chains</u> of carbon atoms with one <u>double bond</u>.
2) They are called <u>unsaturated hydrocarbons</u> because they have some <u>spare bonds</u> left.
3) This is why they <u>will</u> decolourise <u>bromine water</u>. They form <u>bonds</u> with bromide ions.
4) They form <u>polymers</u> by <u>opening up</u> their double bonds to "<u>hold hands</u>" in a long chain.
5) The first three alkenes are <u>ethene</u>, <u>propene</u> and <u>butene</u>.
6) They tend to burn with a <u>smoky flame</u>, producing <u>soot</u> (carbon).

1) Ethene
Formula: C_2H_4

2) Propene
Formula: C_3H_6

3) Butene
Formula: C_4H_8

Important Notes to be noted:

1) <u>Bromine water</u> is the <u>standard test</u> to distinguish between alkanes and alkenes.
2) <u>Alkenes</u> are <u>more reactive</u> due to the <u>double bond</u> all poised and ready to just <u>pop open</u>.
3) Notice the <u>names</u>: "<u>Meth-</u>" means "<u>one</u> carbon atom", "<u>eth-</u>" means "<u>two</u> C atoms", "<u>prop-</u>" means "<u>three</u> C atoms", "<u>but-</u>" means "<u>four</u> C atoms", etc. The only difference then between the names of <u>alkanes</u> and <u>alkenes</u> is just the "<u>-ane</u>" or "<u>-ene</u>" on the end.
4) <u>All alkanes</u> have the formula: C_nH_{2n+2} <u>All alkenes</u> have the formula: C_nH_{2n}

Addition Reactions — Unsaturated becomes Saturated

1) <u>Addition reactions</u> are when one molecule adds to another.
2) <u>Unsaturated</u> hydrocarbons such as <u>alkenes</u> can do this type of reaction because their double bond <u>opens up</u> to form two single bonds. Other atoms can then grab on to one of these new single bonds.
3) Addition reactions turn <u>unsaturated alkenes</u> into <u>saturated</u> compounds, as there are no more spare bonds.
4) Addition reactions are <u>not</u> possible with the <u>alkanes</u> as they don't have double bonds.

Alkane anybody who doesn't learn this lot properly...

It really isn't that difficult to learn the whole page until you can scribble it down from memory.
Try doing it for five minutes: <u>Learn, cover, scribble, check, relearn, cover, scribble, check, etc.</u>

Polymers and Plastics

Polymers and plastics were first discovered in about 1933. By 1970 it was all too late. Those halcyon days when they made proper motor cars with leather seats and lovely wooden dashboards, were over. Sigh.

Alkenes open their double bonds to form Polymers

Under a bit of <u>pressure</u> and with a bit of a <u>catalyst</u> to help it along, many <u>small alkenes</u> will open up their <u>double bonds</u> and "join hands" (polymerisation) to form <u>very long chains</u> called <u>polymers</u>. <u>Ethene</u> becoming polyethene or "polythene", is the easiest example:

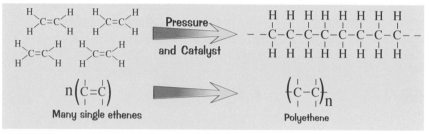

Pressure and Catalyst

Many single ethenes → Polyethene

Other small alkenes do a similar trick:

<u>Propene</u> can form <u>polypropene</u>:

Propene → Polypropene

A molecule called <u>styrene</u> will <u>polymerise</u> into <u>polystyrene</u>:

Styrene → Polystyrene

$\hexagon = C_6H_5$

There are loads of Plastics with loads of different uses

1) Polythene
1) Very <u>cheap</u> and <u>strong</u>
2) Easily <u>moulded</u>

Plastic bags   Bottles   Buckets   Bowls

2) Polypropene
1) Forms <u>strong fibres</u>
2) Has <u>high elasticity</u>

Crates   Ropes   Carpets

3) Polystyrene
1) <u>Cheap</u> and easily <u>moulded</u>
2) Can be <u>expanded</u> into <u>foam</u>

Radio outer cases   Foam packaging

4) PVC (polyvinyl chloride, or polychloroethene)
1) Forms strong waterproof <u>sheets</u>.
2) <u>Hard</u> but <u>flexible</u>.

Plastic sheets   Electric wire insulation   Records

Most plastics don't rot, so they're hard to get rid of

1) Most plastics aren't '<u>biodegradable</u>' — they're not broken down by microorganisms, so they <u>don't rot</u>.
2) It's difficult to get rid of them — if you bury them in a landfill site, they'll <u>still</u> be there <u>years later</u>. The best thing is to <u>recycle</u> them if you can.

Revision — it's all about stringing lots of facts together...

Learn what polymerisation is and practise the set of diagrams for ethene. Also learn all the examples given for the different types of plastics. <u>Then cover the page and scribble it all down.</u>

Metal Ores From the Ground

Rocks, Minerals and Ores

1) A <u>rock</u> is a mixture of <u>minerals</u>.
2) A <u>mineral</u> is any <u>solid element or compound</u> found naturally in the <u>Earth's crust</u>.
   Examples: Diamond (carbon), quartz (silicon dioxide), bauxite (Al_2O_3).
3) A <u>metal ore</u> is defined as a <u>mineral</u> or minerals which contain <u>enough metal</u> in them to make it <u>worthwhile</u> extracting the metal from it.
4) There's a <u>limited amount</u> of minerals and ores — they're "finite resources".

Metals are extracted from ores using Carbon (usually)

1) <u>Extracting a metal</u> from its ore involves a <u>chemical reaction</u> to separate the metal out.
2) In many cases the metal is found as an <u>oxide</u>. A common way of <u>extracting a metal</u> from its ore is chemical <u>reduction</u> using <u>carbon</u> or <u>carbon monoxide</u>.
3) <u>Gold</u> is one of the few metals found as a <u>metal</u> rather than in a chemical compound (an ore).

More Reactive Metals are Harder to Get

1) The <u>more reactive</u> metals took <u>longer</u> to be discovered. (e.g. aluminium, sodium)
2) The <u>more reactive</u> metals are also <u>harder to extract</u> from their mineral ores.
3) The above <u>two facts</u> are obviously <u>related</u>. It's <u>obvious</u> when you think about it...

Even primitive folk could find gold easy enough just by scrabbling about in streams, and then melt it into ingots and jewellery and statues of ABBA during their 1857 comeback tour, but coming up with a fully operational electrolysis plant to extract sodium metal from rock salt, complete with plastic yukkas in the foyer, just by paddling about a bit... unlikely.

The Position of Carbon in the Reactivity Series decides it

1) Metals <u>higher than carbon</u> in the reactivity series can't be extracted using carbon reduction *(they're done using <u>electrolysis</u> instead)*.

2) Metals <u>below carbon</u> in the reactivity series can be extracted by <u>reduction</u> using <u>carbon</u>.

3) This is obviously because carbon <u>can only take the oxygen</u> away from metals which are <u>less reactive</u> than carbon <u>itself</u> is.

THE REACTIVITY SERIES		
Extracted using Electrolysis	Potassium	K
	Sodium	Na
	Calcium	Ca
	Magnesium	Mg
	Aluminium	Al
	CARBON	**C**
Extracted by reduction using carbon	Zinc	Zn
	Iron	Fe
	Tin	Sn
	Lead	Pb

Iron is Extracted from its Ore in a Blast Furnace

Iron is a <u>very common element</u> in the Earth's crust, but good iron ores are only found in <u>a few select places</u> around the world, such as Australia, Canada and Millom.

1) Iron is extracted from <u>haematite</u>, Fe_2O_3, by <u>reduction</u> (removal of oxygen) in a <u>blast furnace</u>.
2) The <u>raw materials</u> are <u>iron ore</u>, <u>coke</u> (pure-ish carbon) and <u>limestone</u> (to remove impurities).
3) <u>Hot air</u> is blasted into the furnace to make the <u>coke burn much faster</u> than normal.
4) The <u>coke</u> reacts with <u>oxygen</u> to form <u>carbon monoxide</u>...
   ... which in turn reacts with the <u>iron ore</u> to form <u>carbon dioxide</u> and <u>iron</u>. IRON ← → SLAG
5) The main <u>impurity</u> is <u>sand</u>, which reacts with the <u>limestone</u> to form <u>carbon dioxide</u> and <u>molten slag</u>.

Miners — they always have to get their ore in...

This page has five sections with three or four important points in each.
They're all important enough to need learning (except the bit about 1857, etc.).
You need to practise <u>repeating</u> the details <u>from memory</u>. That's the <u>only effective method</u>.

Important Uses of Limestone

1) Limestone for Neutralising Acid in Lakes and Soil

This is the equation for <u>any</u> neutralisation reaction. Learn it well:

acid + alkali hydroxide solution $\longrightarrow$ neutral salt solution + water

1) Neutralisation reactions can be used to make <u>fertilisers</u>:

$$HNO_3 + KOH \longrightarrow KNO_3 + H_2O$$

Potassium Nitrate (KNO_3) can be used as a fertiliser.

2) Ordinary limestone <u>ground into powder</u> can be used to <u>neutralise</u> acidity in lakes caused by <u>acid rain</u>.

3) It can also be used to neutralise <u>acid soils</u> in fields.
But it works <u>better</u> and <u>faster</u> if it's turned into <u>slaked lime</u> first.

2) Turning Limestone into Slaked Lime: First Heat it up...

1) <u>Limestone</u> is a <u>sedimentary rock</u>, formed mainly from <u>sea shells</u>. It's mostly <u>calcium carbonate</u>.
2) Limestone can be easily turned into <u>quicklime</u> by heating it.
3) This reaction is a <u>thermal decomposition</u>.

limestone $\xrightarrow{\text{HEAT}}$ quicklime   or $CaCO_3 \xrightarrow{\text{HEAT}} CaO + CO_2$

4) Copper carbonate does pretty much the same thing.

$$CuCO_3 \xrightarrow{\text{HEAT}} CuO + CO_2$$

...then Add Water

1) <u>Calcium oxide</u> reacts <u>violently</u> with <u>water</u> to produce <u>calcium hydroxide</u> (or <u>slaked lime</u>).

quicklime + water $\longrightarrow$ slaked lime   or $CaO + H_2O \longrightarrow Ca(OH)_2$

2) <u>Slaked lime</u> is a <u>white powder</u> and can be applied to fields just like powdered limestone.
3) The <u>advantage</u> is that slaked lime acts much <u>faster</u> to reduce the acidity.

3) Limestone is Used to Make Cement and Glass

1) <u>Clay</u> contains <u>aluminium</u> and <u>silicates</u> and is dug out of the ground.
2) Powdered <u>clay</u> and powdered <u>limestone</u> are <u>roasted</u> in a rotating <u>kiln</u> to produce a complex mixture of calcium and aluminium silicates, called <u>cement</u>.
3) When <u>cement</u> is mixed with <u>water</u> a slow chemical reaction takes place.
4) This causes the cement to gradually <u>set hard</u>.
5) Cement is usually mixed with <u>sand and chippings</u> to make <u>concrete</u>.
6) <u>Concrete</u> is a very quick and cheap way of constructing buildings — and it shows...
— concrete has got to be the most hideously unattractive building material ever known.

1) To make glass, just heat up <u>limestone</u> (calcium carbonate) with <u>sand</u> (silicon dioxide) and <u>soda</u> (sodium carbonate) until it <u>melts</u>.
2) When the mixture cools it comes out as <u>glass</u>. It's as easy as that. Eat your heart out, Mr. Pilkington.

Tough Revision here — this stuff's rock hard...

I bet when those little sea creatures died all those millions of years ago, they had no idea they would one day become the cornerstones of 20th century civilisation. Get it! — cornerstones. Chortle chortle. Anyway, enough frivolity. <u>Learn the whole page</u> till you've got it rock solid...

Using Ammonia to Make Fertilisers

On this page are two reactions involving ammonia that you need to be familiar with. Somehow, I don't think I'd have either of them in my list of "Top Ten Most Riveting Chemistry Topics":

1) Ammonia Can be Oxidised to Form Nitric Acid

There are two stages to this reaction:

a) Ammonia gas reacts with oxygen over a hot platinum catalyst:

$$4NH_{3\,(g)} + 5O_{2\,(g)} \rightarrow 4NO_{\,(g)} + 6H_2O_{\,(g)}$$

This first stage is very exothermic and produces its own heat to keep it going.
The nitrogen monoxide must be cooled before the next stage, which happens easily:

b) The nitrogen monoxide reacts with water and oxygen...

$$6NO_{\,(g)} + 3O_{2\,(g)} + 2H_2O_{\,(g)} \rightarrow 4HNO_{3\,(g)} + 2NO_{\,(g)}$$

...to form nitric acid, HNO_3

Gripping stuff. Anyway, the nitric acid produced is very useful for other chemical processes.
One such use is to make ammonium nitrate fertiliser...

2) Ammonia can be neutralised with Nitric Acid...

...to make Ammonium Nitrate fertiliser

This is a straightforward and spectacularly unexciting neutralisation reaction between an alkali (ammonia) and an acid. The result is of course a neutral salt: *(prod me if I fall asleep)*

$$NH_{3\,(g)} + HNO_{3\,(aq)} \rightarrow NH_4NO_{3\,(aq)}$$
Ammonia + Nitric acid $\rightarrow$ Ammonium nitrate

Ammonium nitrate is an especially good fertiliser because it has nitrogen from two sources, the ammonia and the nitric acid. Kind of a double dose. Plants need nitrogen to make proteins.

Excessive Nitrate Fertiliser causes Eutrophication and Health Problems

1) If nitrate fertilisers wash into streams they set off a cycle of mega-growth, mega-death and mega-decay. Plants and green algae grow out of control, then start to die off because there's too many of them, then bacteria take over, feeding off the dying plants and using up all the oxygen in the water. Then the fish all die because they can't get enough oxygen. Lovely.
It's called eutrophication (See the Section Three for more details). It's all good clean fun.

2) If too many nitrates get into drinking water it can cause health problems, especially for young babies. Nitrates prevent the blood from carrying oxygen properly and children can turn blue and even die.

3) To avoid these problems it's important that artificial nitrate fertilisers are applied carefully by all farmers — they must take care not to apply too much, and not if it's going to rain soon.

Here's your nitric acid sir — don't drink it all at once...

Basically, this page is about how ammonia is turned into ammonium nitrate fertiliser. Alas there are some seriously tedious details which they seem to expect you to learn. Don't ask me why. Anyway, the more you learn, the more you know. (He said, wisely and meaninglessly.)

Revision Summary for Section Four

Section Four is pretty interesting stuff I reckon. Relatively speaking. Anyway, whether it is or it isn't, the only thing that really matters is whether you've learnt it all or not. These questions aren't exactly friendly, but they're a seriously serious way of finding out what you don't know. And don't forget, that's what revision is all about — finding out what you don't know and then learning it till you do. Practise these questions as often as necessary — not just once. Your ultimate aim is to be able to answer all of them easily.

1) Sketch an atom. Give five details about the nucleus and five details about the electrons.
2) What are the three particles found in an atom?
3) Do a table showing their relative masses and charges.
4) How do the numbers of these particles compare to each other in a neutral atom?
5) What do the mass number and atomic number represent?
6) Explain what an isotope is. (!) Give a well-known example.
7) List five facts (or "Rules") about electron shells.
8) What is ionic bonding? Which kind of atoms like to do ionic bonding?
9) Why do atoms want to form ionic bonds anyway?
10) Give full details of the lab tests for:
    Chlorine, oxygen, carbon dioxide, water (3 tests), hydrogen.
11) Sketch the six chemical Hazard Symbols, explain what they mean, and give an example for each.
12) Describe how crude oil is formed. What length of time does it take?
13) What does crude oil consist of?
14) Draw a diagram of the fractional distillation of crude oil.
15) What are the seven main fractions obtained from crude oil?
16) What are hydrocarbons? Describe four properties and how they vary with the molecule size.
17) Give the equations for complete and incomplete combustion of hydrocarbons.
18) Which type is dangerous and why? What colour are the flames for these two types of combustion?
19) What is "cracking"? Why is it done?
20) What are the industrial conditions used for cracking?
21) Give a typical example of a substance which is cracked and the products that you get.
22) What are alkanes and alkenes? What is the basic difference between them?
23) Draw the structures of the first four alkanes and the first three alkenes and give their names.
24) List four differences in the chemical properties of alkanes and alkenes.
25) How can you identify a saturated compound? What about unsaturated compounds?
26) What are polymers? What kind of substances can form polymers?
27) Draw diagrams to show how ethene, propene and styrene form polymers.
28) Name four types of plastic, give their physical properties and say what they're used for.
29) What are rocks, ores and minerals? Name a metal that is found as a metal rather than an ore.
30) What's the main method for extracting metals from their ores?
31) What decides whether this method can be used or not?
32) Describe briefly how a blast furnace works. What are the three raw materials used in it?
33) Name three uses of limestone.
34) Give the equations for turning limestone into slaked lime. Why do we bother?
35) Give four details about what cement is made of and how it works.
36) Give full details of how ammonia is turned into nitric acid, including equations.
37) What is the main use of ammonia? Give the equation for producing ammonium nitrate.
38) Give two problems resulting from nitrate fertilisers. Explain fully what "eutrophication" is.

Nine Types of Chemical Change

There are nine types of chemical change you should know about. It's well worth learning exactly what each of them is, here and now, rather than living the rest of your life in a confused haze.

1) THERMAL DECOMPOSITION — breakdown on heating

This is when a substance breaks down into simpler substances when heated, often with the help of a catalyst. It's different from a reaction because there's only one substance to start with. Cracking of hydrocarbons is a good example of thermal decomposition.

2) NEUTRALISATION — acid + alkali gives salt + water

This is simply when an acid reacts with an alkali (or base) to form a neutral product, which is neither acid nor alkali (usually a salt solution).

3) DISPLACEMENT — one metal kicking another one out

This is a reaction where a more reactive element reacts with a compound and pushes out a less reactive "rival" element. Metals are the most common example. Magnesium will react with iron sulphate to push the iron out and form magnesium sulphate.

4) PRECIPITATION — solid forms in solution

This is a reaction where two solutions react and a solid forms in the solution and sinks. The solid is said to "precipitate out" and, confusingly, the solid is also called "a precipitate".

5) OXIDATION — loss of electrons

Oxidation is the addition of oxygen. Iron becoming iron oxide is oxidation.
The more technical and general definition of oxidation is "the loss of electrons".

Remember
"OIL RIG"
(Oxidation Is Loss,
Reduction Is Gain)

6) REDUCTION — gain of electrons

Reduction is the reverse of oxidation, i.e. the loss of oxygen. Iron oxide is reduced to iron. The more technical and general definition of reduction is "the gain of electrons". Note that reduction is gain of electrons. That's the way to remember it — it's kinda the wrong way round.

7) EXOTHERMIC REACTIONS — give out heat

Exothermic reactions give out energy, usually as heat. "Exo-" as in "Exit", or "out".
Any time a fuel burns and gives off heat it's an exothermic reaction.

8) ENDOTHERMIC REACTIONS — take in heat

Endothermic reactions need heat putting in constantly to make them work. Heat is needed to form chemical bonds. The products of endothermic reactions are likely to be more useful than the reactants, otherwise we wouldn't bother putting all the energy in, e.g. turning iron oxide into iron is an endothermic process. We need a lot of heat from the coke to keep it happening.

9) REVERSIBLE REACTIONS — they go both ways

Reversible reactions are ones that will cheerfully go in both directions at the same time.
In other words, the products can easily turn back into the original reactants.

Nine more fantastic chat-up lines just waiting to happen...

A nice easy page to learn. You should know a lot of this already.
Anyway, cover the page and expose each yellow box (without the other bit of the heading!) one by one and try to explain it to yourself before uncovering the text to check.

A Brief History of The Periodic Table

The early Chemists were keen to try and find <u>patterns</u> in the elements.
The <u>more</u> elements that were identified, the <u>easier</u> it became to find patterns of course.

In the Early 1800s They Could Only go on Atomic Mass

They had <u>two</u> obvious ways to categorise elements:

1) Their <u>physical</u> and <u>chemical properties</u>	2) Their <u>Relative Atomic Mass</u>

1) Remember, they had <u>no idea</u> of <u>atomic structure</u> or of protons or electrons, so there was <u>no such thing</u> as <u>atomic number</u> to them. (It was only in the 20th Century after protons and electrons were discovered, that it was realised the elements should be arranged in order of <u>atomic number</u>.)
2) But <u>back then</u>, the only thing they could measure was <u>Relative Atomic Mass</u> and the only obvious way to arrange the known elements was <u>in order of atomic mass</u>.
3) When this was done a <u>periodic pattern</u> was noticed in the <u>properties</u> of the elements.

Newlands' Octaves Were The First Good Effort

A chap called <u>Newlands</u> had the first good stab at it in <u>1863</u>. He noticed that every <u>eighth</u> element had similar properties and so he listed some of the known elements in rows of seven:

Li	Be	B	C	N	O	F
Na	Mg	Al	Si	P	S	Cl

These sets of eight were called <u>Newlands' Octaves</u> but unfortunately the pattern <u>broke down</u> on the <u>third row</u> with many <u>transition metals</u> like Fe, Cu and Zn messing it up completely.
It was because he left <u>no gaps</u> that his work was <u>ignored</u>.
But he was getting <u>pretty close</u>, as you can see.

Dmitri Mendeleyev Left Gaps and Predicted New Elements

1) In <u>1869</u>, <u>Dmitri Mendeleyev</u> in Russia, armed with about 50 known elements, arranged them into his Table of Elements with various <u>gaps</u>, as shown.
2) Mendeleyev ordered the elements in order of <u>atomic mass</u> (like Newlands did).
3) But Mendeleyev found he had to leave <u>gaps</u> in order to keep elements with <u>similar properties</u> in the same <u>vertical groups</u> — and he was prepared to leave some <u>very big gaps</u> in the first two rows before the transition metals come in on the <u>third</u> row.

The <u>gaps</u> were the really clever bit because they <u>predicted</u> the properties of so far <u>undiscovered elements</u>.

When they were found and they <u>fitted the pattern</u> it was pretty smashing news for old Dmitri. The old rogue.

Mendeleyev's Table of the Elements

H																	
Li	Be											B	C	N	O	F	
Na	Mg											Al	Si	P	S	Cl	
K	Ca	*	Ti	V	Cr	Mn	Fe	Co	Ni	Cu	Zn	*	*	As	Se	Br	
Rb	Sr	Y	Zr	Nb	Mo	*	Ru	Rh	Pd	Ag	Cd	In	Sn	Sb	Te	I	
Cs	Ba	*	*	Ta	W	*	Os	Ir	Pt	Au	Hg	Tl	Pb	Bi			

I can't see what all the fuss is — it all seems quite elementary...

They're quite into having bits of History in Science now. They like to think you'll gain an appreciation of the role of science in the overall progress of human society. Personally, I'm not that bothered whether you do or not. All I wanna know is: <u>Have you learnt all the facts yet?</u> And if not — <u>WHY NOT?</u> HUH?

The Periodic Table

Group O

| | | | | | 4
He
Helium
2 |

Group I Group II

Group III Group IV Group V Group VI Group VII

2	7 Li Lithium 3	9 Be Beryllium 4												11 B Boron 5	12 C Carbon 6	14 N Nitrogen 7	16 O Oxygen 8	19 F Fluorine 9	20 Ne Neon 10
3	23 Na Sodium 11	24 Mg Magnesium 12											27 Al Aluminium 13	28 Si Silicon 14	31 P Phosphorus 15	32 S Sulphur 16	35.5 Cl Chlorine 17	40 Ar Argon 18
4	39 K Potassium 19	40 Ca Calcium 20	45 Sc Scandium 21	48 Ti Titanium 22	51 V Vanadium 23	52 Cr Chromium 24	55 Mn Manganese 25	56 Fe Iron 26	59 Co Cobalt 27	59 Ni Nickel 28	64 Cu Copper 29	65 Zn Zinc 30	70 Ga Gallium 31	73 Ge Germanium 32	75 As Arsenic 33	79 Se Selenium 34	80 Br Bromine 35	84 Kr Krypton 36
5	86 Rb Rubidium 37	88 Sr Strontium 38	89 Y Yttrium 39	91 Zr Zirconium 40	93 Nb Niobium 41	96 Mo Molybdenum 42	99 Tc Technetium 43	101 Ru Ruthenium 44	103 Rh Rhodium 45	106 Pd Palladium 46	108 Ag Silver 47	112 Cd Cadmium 48	115 In Indium 49	119 Sn Tin 50	122 Sb Antimony 51	128 Te Tellurium 52	127 I Iodine 53	131 Xe Xenon 54
6	133 Cs Caesium 55	137 Ba Barium 56	57-71 Lanthanides	179 Hf Hafnium 72	181 Ta Tantalum 73	184 W Tungsten 74	186 Re Rhenium 75	190 Os Osmium 76	192 Ir Iridium 77	195 Pt Platinum 78	197 Au Gold 79	201 Hg Mercury 80	204 Tl Thallium 81	207 Pb Lead 82	209 Bi Bismuth 83	210 Po Polonium 84	210 At Astatine 85	222 Rn Radon 86
7	223 Fr Francium 87	226 Ra Radium 88	89-103 Actinides															

1
H
Hydrogen
1

mass number → 4
He
Helium
atomic number → 2

reactive metals

transition elements

poor metals

non metals

noble gases

separates metals from non-metals

The Periodic Table is Ace

1) There are 100ish elements, which all materials are made of. More are still being discovered.
2) The <u>modern</u> Periodic Table shows the elements in order of <u>atomic number</u>.
3) The Periodic Table is laid out so that elements with <u>similar properties</u> form in <u>columns</u>.
4) These <u>vertical columns</u> are called <u>Groups</u> and Roman Numerals are often used for them.
5) For example the <u>Group II</u> elements are Be, Mg, Ca, Sr, Ba and Ra.
   They're all <u>metals</u> which form 2+ ions and they have many other <u>similar properties</u>.
6) The <u>rows</u> are called <u>periods</u>. Each <u>new period</u> represents <u>another full shell</u> of electrons.

The Elements of a Group Have the Same Outer Electrons

1) The elements in each <u>Group</u> all have the same number of <u>electrons</u> in their <u>outer shell</u>.
2) That's why they have <u>similar properties</u>. And that's why we arrange them in this way.
3) You absolutely must get that into your head if you want to <u>understand</u> any Chemistry.

   The properties of the elements are decided <u>*entirely*</u> by how many electrons they have.
   Atomic number is therefore very significant because it is equal to how many electrons each atom has.
   But it's the number of electrons in the <u>*outer shell*</u> which is the really important thing.

Electron Shells are just Totally Brill

The fact that electrons form shells around atoms is the reason for the whole of chemistry.
If they just whizzed round the nucleus any old how and didn't care about shells or any of that stuff there'd be no chemical reactions. No nothing in fact — because nothing would happen.
   Without shells there'd be no atoms wanting to gain, lose or share electrons to form full shell arrangements. So they wouldn't be interested in forming ions or covalent bonds. Nothing would bother and nothing would happen. The atoms would just slob about, all day long. Just like teenagers.
   But amazingly, they *do* form shells (if they didn't, we wouldn't even be here to wonder about it), and the electron arrangement of each atom determines the whole of its chemical behaviour.
Phew. I mean electron arrangements explain practically the whole Universe. They're just totally brill.

Electron Shells — where would we be without them...

Make sure you learn the whole periodic table including every name, symbol and number.
No, only kidding! Just <u>learn</u> the numbered points and <u>scribble</u> them down, <u>mini-essay style</u>.

Electron Arrangements

This diagram shows the electron arrangements of the first twenty elements. Learn it real good.

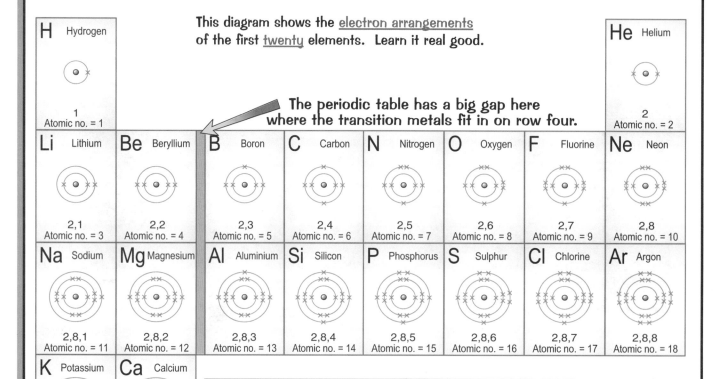

The periodic table has a big gap here where the transition metals fit in on row four.

Higher

Reactivity Changes down the Groups due to Shielding

1) As Atoms get bigger, they have more full shells of electrons.
2) As you go down any Group, each new row has one more full shell.
3) The number of outer electrons is the same for each element in a Group.
4) However the outer shell of electrons is increasingly far from the nucleus.
5) You have to learn to say that the inner shells provide "SHIELDING".
6) This means that the outer shell electrons get shielded from the attraction of the +ve nucleus. The upshot of all this is:

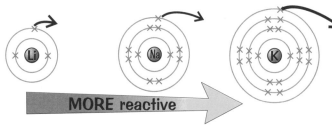

MORE reactive

As metal atoms get bigger, the outer electron is more easily lost.

This makes *METALS MORE REACTIVE* as you go *DOWN* Group I and Group II

Higher

As non-metal atoms get bigger, the extra electrons are harder to gain.

This makes *NON-METALS LESS REACTIVE* as you go *DOWN* Group VI and Group VII

LESS reactive

Higher

Learn about Electron Shielding — and keep up with the trends...

Really, you should know enough about electron shells to do that whole diagram at the top of the page without looking at it. Obviously you don't learn every atom separately — you learn the pattern. Also learn about the trends in reactivity. Then cover the page and see what you know — by scribbling.

The Noble Gases and The Alkali Metals

Group 0 — The Noble Gases

As you go down the group:

1) Density _increases_
2) Boiling point _increases_

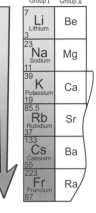

1) The Noble Gases are _inert_ — i.e. they _don't_ _react_ with anything.

2) _Helium_, _Neon_ and _Argon_ are examples of Noble gases.

3) They're all _colourless gases_.

4) They all exist as _individual atoms_ (because they won't form bonds with anything).

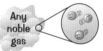
Any noble gas

5) _Helium_ is used in _Airships_ and _Party Balloons_ — it's ideal because it has very low density and won't set on fire, (like hydrogen does!).

Helium is ace!
I love Helium
And safe too!

6) _Neon_ is used in _electrical discharge tubes_ — when a current is passed through neon it gives out a _bright light_.

NEON IS ACE

7) _Argon_ is used in filament lamps (_light bulbs_) — it provides an inert atmosphere which stops the very hot filament from burning away.

All these bulbs, argon
Eh? They look O.K. to me

8) All three are used in _lasers_ too. There's the famous little red _Helium-Neon laser_ and the more powerful _Argon laser_.

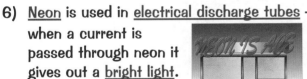

He-Ne laser O - oh
Argon laser

Group 1 — The Alkali Metals

As you go down the group:

1) _Atoms_ get bigger
2) _Reactivity increases_
3) _Density increases_
4) Metals are _softer_ to cut
5) Melting point _decreases_
6) Boiling point _decreases_

1) The _Alkali Metals_ are _very reactive_ — they have to be stored in _oil_ and handled with _forceps_ (they burn the skin).

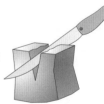

2) _Lithium_, _Sodium_ and _Potassium_ are the main ones to remember.

3) The alkali metals have _one electron_ in their _outer shell_. This is what makes them _very reactive_.

4) The Alkali metals are _soft_ — they _cut with a knife_. They're _shiny_ when freshly cut, but _soon go dull_ as they react with the air.

5) They _melt_ and _boil easily_ (compared with other metals).

6) They have _low density_. Lithium, Sodium and Potassium are less dense than _water_ — so they _float_.

Inert Gases don't react — that's Noble De-use to us Chemists...

There's plenty of stuff to learn about these two groups. Nevertheless, they're likely to ask questions on them so _make sure you learn everything on this page_. Particularly the _trends_.

62

Reactions of the Alkali Metals

Reaction with Cold Water produces Hydrogen Gas

1) When <u>lithium</u>, <u>sodium</u> or <u>potassium</u> are put in <u>water</u>, they react very <u>vigorously</u>.

2) They <u>move</u> around the surface, <u>fizzing</u> furiously.

3) They produce <u>hydrogen</u>. Potassium gets hot enough to <u>ignite</u> it. A lighted splint will <u>indicate</u> hydrogen by producing the notorious "<u>squeaky pop</u>" as the H_2 ignites.

4) Sodium and potassium <u>melt</u> in the heat of the reaction.

5) They form a <u>hydroxide</u> in solution.

The solution becomes <u>alkaline</u>, which changes the colour of the pH indicator to <u>purple</u>.

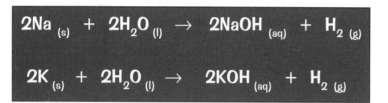

$$2Na_{(s)} + 2H_2O_{(l)} \rightarrow 2NaOH_{(aq)} + H_{2(g)}$$

$$2K_{(s)} + 2H_2O_{(l)} \rightarrow 2KOH_{(aq)} + H_{2(g)}$$

Alkali Metal Oxides and Hydroxides are Alkaline

This means that they'll react with <u>acids</u> to form <u>neutral salts</u>, like this:

$$NaOH + HCl \rightarrow H_2O + NaCl \text{ (salt)}$$

$$Na_2O + 2HCl \rightarrow H_2O + 2NaCl \text{ (salt)}$$

All Alkali Compounds look like 'Salt' and Dissolve with Glee

1) All alkali metal compounds form <u>crystals</u> which <u>dissolve</u> easily.

2) The compounds are all very <u>stable</u> because the alkali metals are so <u>reactive</u>.

3) Because they always form <u>ionic</u> compounds with <u>giant ionic lattices</u> the compounds <u>all</u> look pretty much like the regular 'salt' you put in your chip butties.

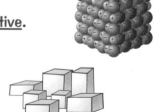

The Notorious Squeaky Pop? — weren't they a Rock Band...

This stuff's pretty grisly isn't it. Still, if you keep covering the page and repeating bits back to yourself, or scribbling bits down, then little by little <u>it does go in</u>. Little by little. <u>Nicely</u>.

Section Five — Reactions and Periodic Trends

Group VII — The Halogens

There are four halogens you need to know about: <u>Fluorine</u>, <u>Chlorine</u>, <u>Bromine</u> and <u>Iodine</u>.

Learn These Trends:

As you go <u>*DOWN*</u> Group VII, the <u>*HALOGENS*</u> have the following properties:

1) *Less Reactive*
2) *Higher melting point*
3) *Higher boiling point*

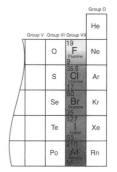

Learn the <u>states</u> of the halogens at <u>room temperature</u>:

Fluorine: Gas	Chlorine: Gas	Bromine: Liquid	Iodine: Solid

1) The Halogens are all non-metals with coloured vapours

<u>Fluorine</u> is a very reactive, poisonous, <u>yellow gas</u>.
<u>Chlorine</u> is a fairly reactive, poisonous, <u>dense green gas</u>.
<u>Bromine</u> is a dense, poisonous, <u>red-brown volatile liquid</u>.
<u>Iodine</u> is a <u>dark grey</u> crystalline <u>solid</u> or a <u>purple vapour</u>.

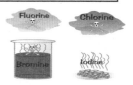

2) The Halogens react with metals to form salts

They react with most metals including <u>iron</u> and <u>aluminium</u>, to form <u>salts</u> (or '<u>metal halides</u>').

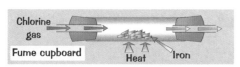

$$2Na_{(s)} + Cl_{2(g)} \rightarrow 2NaCl_{(s)}$$
(Sodium chloride)

$$2Fe_{(s)} + 3Br_{2(g)} \rightarrow 2FeBr_{3(s)}$$
(Iron(III) bromide)

3) More reactive Halogens will displace less reactive ones

<u>Chlorine</u> can displace <u>bromine</u> and <u>iodine</u> from a solution of <u>bromide</u> or <u>iodide</u>. <u>Bromine</u> will also displace <u>iodine</u> because of the <u>trend</u> in <u>reactivity</u>.

Cl$_2$ gas

Solution of Potassium iodide

Iodine forming in solution

$$Cl_{2(g)} + 2KI_{(aq)} \rightarrow I_{2(aq)} + 2KCl_{(aq)}$$
$$Cl_{2(g)} + 2KBr_{(aq)} \rightarrow Br_{2(aq)} + 2KCl_{(aq)}$$

4) Halogens react with hydrogen

The halogens form <u>covalent compounds</u> with <u>hydrogen</u>. Fluorine and chlorine can explode as they react with hydrogen. Bromine and iodine only react slowly.

Equations:

$$F_{2(g)} + H_{2(g)} \rightarrow 2HF_{(g)}$$
$$Cl_{2(g)} + H_{2(g)} \rightarrow 2HCl_{(g)}$$

Chlorine is used in bleach and for sterilising water

1) <u>Chlorine</u> dissolved in <u>sodium hydroxide</u> solution is called <u>bleach</u>.

2) <u>Chlorine compounds</u> are also used to <u>kill germs</u> in swimming pools and drinking water.

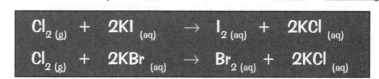

Iodine is used as an antiseptic...

...but it stings like nobody's business and stains the skin <u>brown</u>. Nice.

I've never liked Halogens — they give me a bad head...

I think Halogens are as exciting as white-water rafting (ahem). They change colour and go from gases to liquid to solid. What could be more fun than that. Anyway, <u>just learn the facts</u>.

Acids and Alkalis

The pH Scale and Universal Indicator

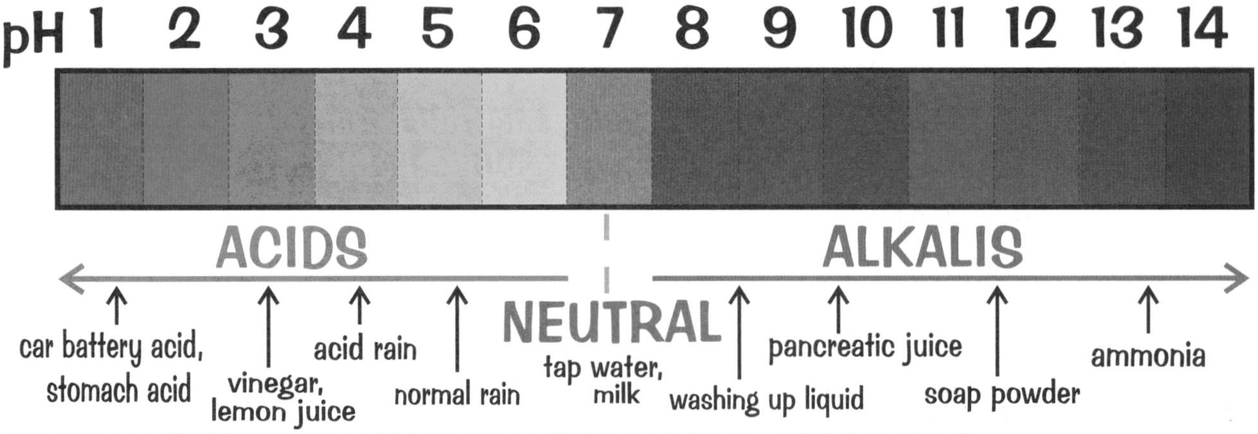

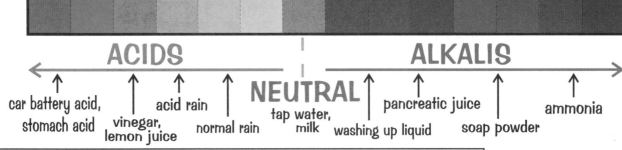

An Indicator is just a Dye that changes colour

The dye <u>changes colour</u> depending on whether it's <u>in an acid</u> or <u>in an alkali</u>.
<u>Universal indicator</u> is a very useful <u>combination of dyes</u> which give the colours shown above.

The pH scale goes from 1 to 14

1) The <u>strongest acid</u> has <u>pH 1</u>. The <u>strongest alkali</u> has <u>pH 14</u>.
2) If something is <u>neutral</u> it has <u>pH 7</u> (e.g. pure water).
3) Anything <u>less</u> than 7 is <u>acid</u>. Anything <u>more</u> than 7 is <u>alkaline</u>. (An alkali can also be called a base.)

Acids have H⁺ ions   *Alkalis have OH⁻ ions*

The <u>strict definitions</u> of acids and alkalis are:

> <u>*ACIDS*</u> are substances which form $\underline{H^+_{(aq)}}$ <u>*ions*</u> when added to <u>*water*</u>.
>
> <u>*ALKALIS*</u> are substances which form $\underline{OH^-_{(aq)}}$ <u>*ions*</u> when added to <u>*water*</u>.

Higher

Neutralisation

This is the equation for <u>any neutralisation reaction</u>. Make sure you learn it:

$$Acid \ + \ alkali \ \rightarrow \ salt \ + \ water$$

Neutralisation can also be seen <u>in terms of ions</u> like this, so learn it too:

$$H^+_{(aq)} \ + \ OH^-_{(aq)} \ \rightarrow \ H_2O_{(l)}$$

Higher

Three "Real life" Examples of Neutralisation:

1) <u>Indigestion</u> is caused by too much <u>hydrochloric acid</u> in the <u>stomach</u>.
   <u>Indigestion tablets</u> contain <u>alkalis</u> such as <u>magnesium oxide</u>, which <u>neutralise</u> the <u>excess HCl</u>.

2) <u>Fields</u> with <u>acidic soils</u> can be improved no end by adding <u>lime</u> (See P. 54).
   The lime added to fields is <u>calcium hydroxide</u> $Ca(OH)_2$ which is of course an <u>alkali</u>.

3) <u>Lakes</u> affected by <u>acid rain</u> can also be <u>neutralised</u> by adding <u>lime</u>. This saves the fish.

Hey man, like "acid", yeah — eeuuucch...

Try and enjoy this page on acids and alkalis, because it gets really tedious from now on. These
are very basic facts and possibly quite interesting. <u>Cover the page and scribble them down.</u>

Acids and their Reactions

Acid + Metal → Salt + Hydrogen

That's written big 'cos it's kinda worth remembering. Here's the typical experiment:

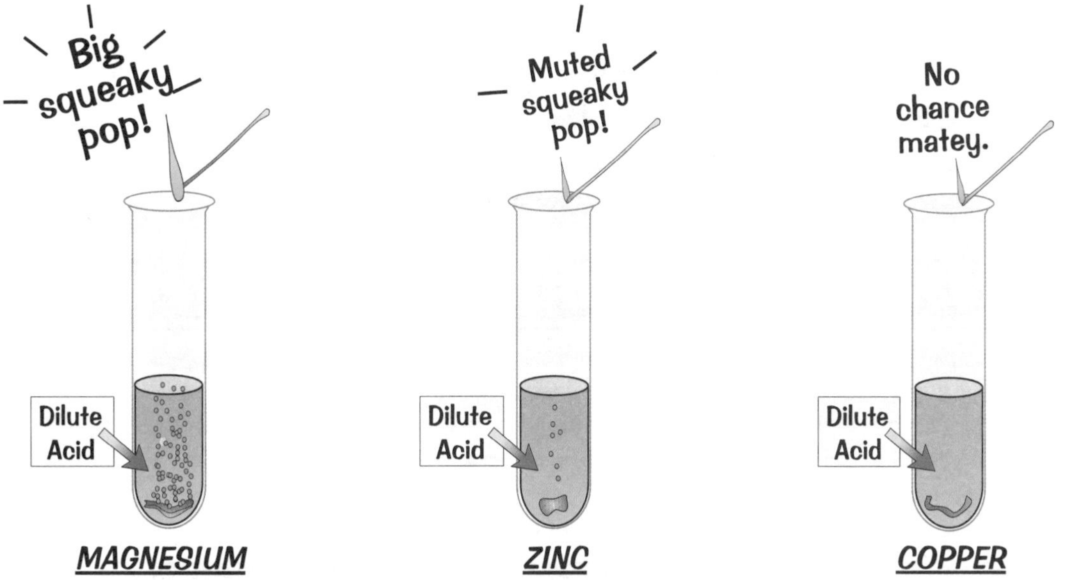
Big squeaky pop!
Muted squeaky pop!
No chance matey.
Dilute Acid
Dilute Acid
Dilute Acid
MAGNESIUM
ZINC
COPPER

Copper is *less reactive* than *hydrogen* so it doesn't react with dilute acids at all.

1) The more reactive the metal, the faster it will go.
2) Copper does not react with dilute acids at all — because it's less reactive than hydrogen.
3) The speed of reaction is indicated by the rate at which the bubbles of hydrogen are given off.
4) The hydrogen is confirmed by the burning splint test giving the notorious "squeaky pop".
5) The type of salt produced depends on which metal is used, and which acid is used:

Higher

Hydrochloric acid will always produce chloride salts:

$2HCl + Mg \rightarrow MgCl_2 + H_2$ (Magnesium chloride)

$2HCl + Zn \rightarrow ZnCl_2 + H_2$ (Zinc chloride)

Sulphuric acid will always produce sulphate salts:

$H_2SO_4 + Mg \rightarrow MgSO_4 + H_2$ (Magnesium sulphate)

$H_2SO_4 + Zn \rightarrow ZnSO_4 + H_2$ (Zinc sulphate)

Nitric acid produces nitrate salts when NEUTRALISED, but...

Nitric acid reacts fine with alkalis, to produce nitrates, but it can play silly devils with metals and produce nitrogen oxides instead, so we'll ignore it here. Chemistry's a real messy subject sometimes, innit.

Higher

Revision of Acids and Metals — easy as squeaky pop...

Actually, this stuff isn't too bad I don't think. I mean it's fairly interesting. Not quite in the same league as base jumping, I grant you, but for Chemistry it's not bad at all. At least there's bubbles and flames and noise and that kinda thing. Anyway, learn it, scribble it down, etc...

Acids and their Reactions

Metal Oxides and Metal Hydroxides are Alkalis

1) Some metal oxides and metal hydroxides dissolve in water to produce alkaline solutions.
2) In other words, metal oxides and metal hydroxides are generally alkalis.
3) This means they'll react with acids to form a salt and water.
4) Even those that won't dissolve in water will still react with acid.

| Acid + Metal Oxide → Salt + Water |

| Acid + Metal Hydroxide → Salt + Water |

(These are neutralisation reactions of course. You can use an indicator to tell when they've reacted completely.)

The Oxides of non-metals are usually Acidic, not akaline

1) The best examples are the oxides of these three non-metals: carbon, sulphur and nitrogen.
2) Carbon dioxide dissolves in water to form carbonic acid which is a weak acid.
3) Sulphur Dioxide combines with water and O_2 to form sulphuric acid which is a strong acid.
4) Nitrogen dioxide dissolves in water to form nitric acid which is a strong acid.
5) These three are all present in acid rain of course.
6) The carbonic acid is present in rain anyway, so even ordinary rain is slightly acidic.

> **Remember these three examples:**
> Carbon dioxide   Sulphur dioxide   Nitrogen dioxide

Acids with Carbonates — Salt, Water and CO_2

More gripping reactions involving acids. At least there's some bubbles involved here.

| Acid + Carbonate → Salt + Water + Carbon dioxide |

| Acid + Hydrogencarbonate → Salt + Water + Carbon dioxide |

1) Definitely learn the fact that carbonates and hydrogencarbonates give off carbon dioxide.
2) Learn this example:
   hydrochloric acid + sodium carbonate →
       sodium chloride + water + carbon dioxide
3) And learn how to test for carbon dioxide —
   it turns limewater milky.

Bubble the gas through limewater. If it's carbon dioxide, the limewater turns milky.

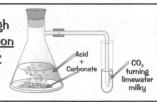

Acids with Ammonia — Ammonium Salt

| Dilute Acid + Ammonia → Ammonium salt |

Learn that, then learn these examples:
1) Hydrochloric acid + Ammonia → Ammonium chloride
2) Nitric acid + Ammonia → Ammonium nitrate ⟵

This last reaction with nitric acid produces the famous ammonium nitrate fertiliser, much appreciated for its double dose of essential nitrogen. (See P.55)

Acids are really dull, aren't they — learn and snore...

Phew, that's it on acids, thank goodness. Learn the last of these dreary facts and try to scribble it down. (If there's an Acid Appreciation Action Group, they're sure gonna be after me.)

Properties of Metals and Non-Metals

About $\frac{3}{4}$ of elements are metals.

All these elements are metals
Just look at 'em all
— there's loads of 'em!

Only these squiddy few are non-metals

About $\frac{1}{4}$ aren't.

Metals are Great Conductors

Higher

The Metallic Crystal Structure

1) <u>All</u> metals have the <u>same</u> basic properties due to the <u>special type of bonding</u> that exists in metals.
2) Metals have a <u>giant structure</u> of atoms held together with <u>metallic bonds</u>.
3) These special bonds allow the <u>outer electron(s)</u> of each atom to <u>move freely</u>.
4) This creates a "<u>sea</u>" of <u>free electrons</u> throughout the metal that gives rise to many of the properties of metals.

Higher

1) Metals all <u>conduct electricity</u> — due to the free electrons which carry the current.

2) They're all <u>good conductors</u> of <u>heat</u> — again this is entirely due to the free electrons which carry the heat energy through the metal.

3) Metals are <u>strong</u> and can be <u>bent</u> into different shapes.

Don't try this at home. You'll die.

4) They're all <u>shiny</u> (when freshly cut or polished).

5) They have <u>high melting and boiling points</u> — e.g. copper 1100°C, tungsten 3377°C. This means you have to get them pretty hot to melt them (except good old mercury).

6) They can be mixed together to form useful <u>alloys</u> (mixtures) — e.g. <u>steel</u> (iron + carbon), <u>bronze</u> (copper + tin) and <u>cupro-nickel</u> (copper + nickel)

Non-Metals are either dull, brittle solids or they're gases

1) Non-metals are poor conductors of heat.
2) They don't conduct electricity at all.
(Except for graphite, and some semiconductors such as silicon.)
3) Non-metals usually bond in small molecules, e.g. O_2 N_2 etc.
4) But carbon is weird — it forms giant structures.

<u>Graphite</u>
(pure carbon)

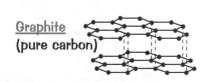

<u>Diamond</u>
(pure carbon)

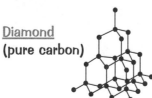

Metal Fatigue? — yeah, we've all had enough of this page now...
Phew.

The Reactivity Series of Metals

You must learn this Reactivity Series

You really should know which are the more reactive metals and which are the less reactive ones.

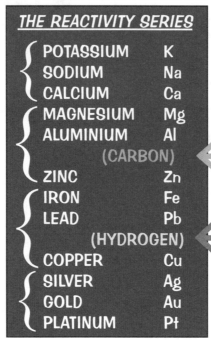

THE REACTIVITY SERIES

POTASSIUM	K
SODIUM	Na
CALCIUM	Ca
MAGNESIUM	Mg
ALUMINIUM	Al
(CARBON)	
ZINC	Zn
IRON	Fe
LEAD	Pb
(HYDROGEN)	
COPPER	Cu
SILVER	Ag
GOLD	Au
PLATINUM	Pt

Very Reactive

Fairly Reactive

Not very Reactive

Not at all Reactive

Metals <u>above carbon</u> must be extracted from their ores by <u>electrolysis</u>.

Metals <u>below carbon</u> can be extracted from their ore using <u>reduction</u> with <u>coke or charcoal</u>.

Metals <u>below hydrogen</u> don't react with <u>water</u> or <u>acid</u>. They don't easily <u>tarnish</u> or <u>corrode</u>.

...and the Reactions with Water, Air and Dilute Acid

This <u>reactivity series</u> was determined by doing <u>experiments</u> to see <u>how strongly</u> metals <u>react</u>. The <u>standard reaction</u> to determine reactivity is with <u>water</u>.
It's <u>important</u> so make sure you know about it in reasonable detail, as follows:

Reaction with Water

POTASSIUM
SODIUM
CALCIUM — React with cold water

MAGNESIUM
ALUMINIUM
ZINC — React with steam

IRON — Reacts reversibly with steam

LEAD
COPPER
SILVER
GOLD — No reaction with water or steam

... and the reactions with air...

Reaction with Air

POTASSIUM
SODIUM
CALCIUM
MAGNESIUM — Burn very easily with a bright flame

ALUMINIUM
ZINC
IRON
LEAD
COPPER — React slowly with air when heated

SILVER
GOLD — No reaction

... and with dilute acid.

Reaction with Dilute Acid

POTASSIUM
SODIUM
CALCIUM — Violent reaction with dilute acids

MAGNESIUM
ALUMINIUM
ZINC
IRON — React fairly well with dilute acids

LEAD
COPPER
SILVER
GOLD — No reaction with dilute acids

How to get a good reaction — just smile ... ☺

Believe it or not they could easily give you a question asking if copper's more reactive than lead, or what happens when calcium is heated in water. That means <u>all these details need learning</u>.

Transition Metals

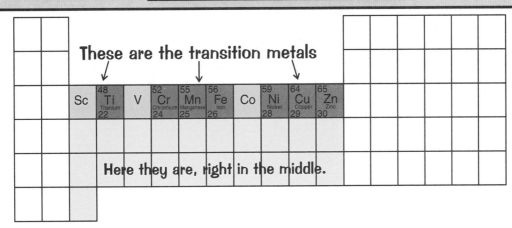

These are the transition metals

Here they are, right in the middle.

Titanium, Chromium, Manganese, Iron, Nickel, Copper, Zinc

You need to know the ones shown in red fairly well. If they wanted to be mean in the Exam *(if!)*
they could cheerfully mention one of the others like scandium or cobalt or vanadium.
Don't let it hassle you. They'll just be testing how well you can *"apply scientific knowledge to
new information"*. In other words, just assume these "new" transition metals follow all the
properties you've already learnt for the others. That's all it is, but it can really worry some folk.

Transition Metals *all have high melting point and high density*

They're <u>typical metals</u>. They have the properties you would expect of a proper metal:
1) <u>Good conductors</u> of heat and electricity. They're very <u>dense</u>, <u>strong</u> and <u>shiny</u>.
2) Iron melts at 1500°C, copper melts at 1100°C and zinc melts at 400°C.

The compounds *are very colourful*

1) The <u>compounds</u> are <u>colourful</u> due to the <u>transition metal ion</u> they contain. e.g. <u>Potassium
   chromate(VI)</u> is yellow. <u>Potassium manganate(VII)</u> is purple. <u>Copper(II) sulphate</u> is blue.
2) The colour of people's <u>hair</u> and also the colours in <u>gemstones</u>, like <u>blue sapphires</u> and <u>green emeralds</u>,
   and the colours in <u>pottery glazes</u> are all due to <u>transition metals</u>.
   ...And weathered (oxidised) <u>copper</u> is a lovely colourful <u>green</u>.

Transition Metals *often have more than one ion*, e.g. Fe^{2+}, Fe^{3+}

Two other examples are <u>copper</u>: Cu^+ and Cu^{2+} and <u>chromium</u>: Cr^{2+} and Cr^{3+}
The <u>different ions</u> usually have <u>different colours</u> too:
Fe^{2+} <u>ions</u> usually give <u>green</u> compounds, whereas Fe^{3+} <u>ions</u> are usually <u>red/brown</u> (rust!)

Uses of Iron, Copper, Zinc and Titanium

1) <u>Iron</u> is used for <u>man-hole covers</u>. <u>Pure iron</u> is very <u>brittle</u>, unlike steel which is more useful.
2) <u>Copper</u> is used for <u>electric wiring</u> and household <u>water pipes</u>. Copper and <u>nickel</u> make <u>coins</u>.
3) <u>Zinc</u> is used for <u>galvanising</u> iron. <u>Zinc</u> and <u>copper</u> make the alloy <u>brass</u> for trumpets and tubas.
4) <u>Titanium</u> is used to make <u>strong</u>, <u>light</u> alloys for aircraft and missiles.

Lots of pretty colours — that's what we like to see...

There's quite a few things to learn about transition metals. First try to remember the five
headings. Then learn the details that go under each one. <u>Keep trying to scribble it all down</u>.

Revision Summary for Section Five

Phew — into proper full-on Chemistry here. All I can say is just keep at it. These are searching questions, it's true — that's to give you some idea of how well you're doing. Don't skip them just because this was a tricky section. If it's tricky, you've got more learning to do. Look up the tricky ones in this section, then come back to the questions and try them again. Keep going until you can answer every question. I'm not joking, you'll be totally stuck in the exam if you don't learn this now.

1) Describe each of these nine types of chemical change: Thermal decomposition, neutralisation, displacement, precipitation, oxidation, reduction, exothermic, endothermic, reversible.
2) What two properties did they base the early periodic table on?
3) Who was the old rogue who had the best shot at it and why was his table so clever?
4) What feature of atoms determines the order of the modern Periodic Table?
5) What are the Periods and Groups? Explain their significance in terms of electrons.
6) Draw diagrams to show the electron arrangements for the first twenty elements.
7) Explain the trend in reactivity of metals and non-metals using the notion of "shielding".
8) What are the properties of the noble gases?
9) Give two uses each for helium, neon and argon.
10) Which Group are the Alkali metals? What is their outer shell like?
11) List four properties of the alkali metals.
12) Give details of the reactions of the alkali metals with water.
13) What can you say about the pH of alkali metal oxides and hydroxides?
14) Describe the trends in appearance and reactivity of the halogens as you go down the Group.
15) List four properties common to all the halogens.
16) Give details, with equations, of the reaction of the halogens with metals.
17) Give details, with equations, of the displacement reactions of the halogens.
18) Describe fully the colour of universal indicator for every pH value from 1 to 14.
19) What type of ions are always present in a) acids and   b) alkalis? What is neutralisation?
20) What is the equation for reacting acid with metal? Which metal(s) don't react with acid?
21) What type of salts do hydrochloric acid and sulphuric acid produce?
22) What type of reaction is "acid + metal oxide", or "acid + metal hydroxide"?
23) What about the oxides of non-metals — are they acidic or alkaline?
24) What are the equations for reacting acids with carbonates and hydrogencarbonates?
25) What is the equation for reacting dilute acid with ammonia?
26) What proportion of the elements are metals? What do all metals contain?
27) List six properties of metals. List four properties of non-metals.
28) Write down the twelve common metals in the order of the Reactivity Series.
29) Where do carbon and hydrogen fit in and what is the significance of their positions?
30) Describe the reaction of all twelve metals with water (or steam). Do the same for air and dilute acid.
31) List four properties of transition metals, and one property of their compounds.
32) Name six transition metals, and give uses for three of them.

Section Five — Reactions and Periodic Trends

Rates of Reaction

Reactions can go at all sorts of different rates

1) One of the slowest is the rusting of iron (it's not slow enough though — what about my little MGB).
2) Other slow reactions include chemical weathering, like acid rain damage to limestone buildings.
3) A moderate speed reaction is a metal (like magnesium) reacting with acid to produce a gentle stream of bubbles.
4) A really fast reaction is an explosion, where it's all over in a fraction of a second.

Three ways to Measure the Speed of a Reaction

The speed of reaction can be observed either by how quickly the reactants are used up or how quickly the products are forming. It's usually a lot easier to measure products forming.
There are three different ways that the speed of a reaction can be measured:

1) Precipitation

This is when the product of the reaction is a precipitate which clouds the solution. Observe a marker through the solution and measure how long it takes for it to disappear.

2) Change in mass (usually gas given off)

Any reaction that produces a gas can be carried out on a mass balance and as the gas is released the mass disappearing is easily measured.

3) The volume of gas given off

This involves the use of a gas syringe to measure the volume of gas given off. But that's about all there is to it.

The Rate of a Reaction Depends on Four Things:

1) TEMPERATURE
2) CONCENTRATION — (or PRESSURE for gases)
3) CATALYST
4) SIZE OF PARTICLES — (or SURFACE AREA)

LEARN THEM!

Typical Graphs for Rate of Reaction

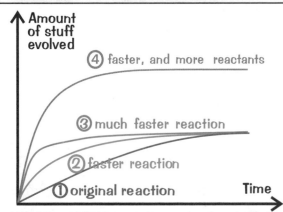

Amount of stuff evolved

④ faster, and more reactants
③ much faster reaction
② faster reaction
① original reaction

Time

1) Graph 1 represents the original fairly slow reaction.
2) Graphs 2 and 3 represent the reaction taking place quicker but with the same initial amounts.
3) The increased rate could be due to any of these:

> a) increase in temperature
> b) increase in concentration (or pressure)
> c) solid reactant crushed up into smaller bits
> d) catalyst added.

4) Graph 4 produces more product as well as going quicker. This can only happen if more reactant(s) are added at the start.

How to get a fast, furious reaction — crack a wee joke...

There's all sorts of bits and bobs of information on this page. To learn it all, you've got to learn to split it up into separate sections and do them one at a time. Practise by covering the page and seeing how much you can scribble down for each section. Then try again, and again...

Collision Theory

Reaction rates are explained perfectly by Collision Theory. It's really simple. It just says that the rate of a reaction simply depends on how often and how hard the reacting particles collide with each other. The basic idea is that particles have to collide in order to react, and they have to collide hard enough as well.

More Collisions increases the Rate of Reaction

All the methods of increasing the rate of reactions can be explained in terms of increasing the number of collisions between the reacting particles;

1) TEMPERATURE increases the number of collisions

When the temperature is increased the particles all move quicker. If they're moving quicker, they're going to have more collisions.

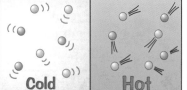

2) CONCENTRATION (or PRESSURE) increases the number of collisions

If the solution is made more concentrated it means there are more particles of reactant knocking about between the water molecules which makes collisions between the important particles more likely. In a gas, increasing the pressure means the molecules are more squashed up together so there are going to be more collisions.

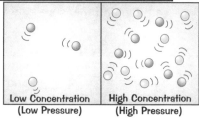

3) SIZE OF SOLID PARTICLES (or SURFACE AREA) increases collisions

If one of the reactants is a solid then breaking it up into smaller pieces will increase its surface area. This means the particles around it in the solution will have more area to work on so there'll be more useful collisions.

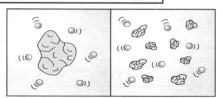

4) CATALYST increases the number of collisions

A catalyst works by giving the reacting particles a surface to stick to where they can bump into each other. This obviously increases the number of collisions too.

Faster Collisions increase the Rate of Reaction

Higher temperature also increases the energy of the collisions, because it makes all the particles move faster.

Faster collisions are ONLY caused by increasing the temperature

Reactions only happen if the particles collide with enough energy. At a higher temperature there will be more particles colliding with enough energy to make the reaction happen. This initial energy is known as the activation energy, and it's needed to break the initial bonds.

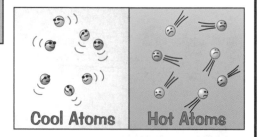

Collision Theory — I reckon it's always the other driver...

This is quite easy I think. Isn't it all kind of obvious — at least once you've been told it, anyway. The more often particles collide and the harder they hit, the greater the reaction rate. There's a few extra picky details of course (isn't there always!), but you've only got to LEARN them...

Four Experiments on Rate of Reaction 1

REMEMBER: Any reaction can be used to investigate any of the four factors that affect the rate. These pages illustrate four important reactions, but only one factor has been considered for each. But we could just as easily use, say, the marble chips/acid reaction to test the effect of temperature instead.

1) Reaction of Hydrochloric Acid and Marble Chips

This experiment is often used to demonstrate the effect of breaking the solid up into small bits.

1) Measure the volume of gas evolved with a gas syringe and take readings at regular intervals.

2) Make a table of readings and plot them as a graph.

3) Repeat the experiment with exactly the same volume of acid, and exactly the same mass of marble chips, but with the marble more crunched up.

4) Then repeat with the same mass of powdered chalk instead of marble chips.

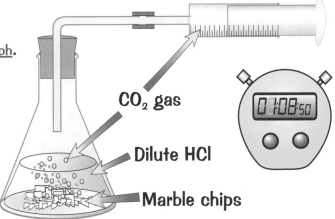

CO_2 gas

Dilute HCl

Marble chips

These graphs show the effect of using finer particles of solid

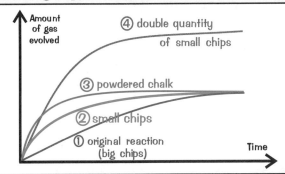

Amount of gas evolved

④ double quantity of small chips

③ powdered chalk

② small chips

① original reaction (big chips)

Time

1) The increase in surface area causes more collisions so the rate of reaction is faster.

2) Graph 4 shows the reaction if a greater mass of small marble chips is added.

3) The extra surface area gives a quicker reaction and there is also more gas evolved overall.

2) Reaction of Magnesium Metal With Dilute HCl

1) This reaction is good for measuring the effects of increased concentration, (as is the marble/acid reaction).

2) This reaction gives off hydrogen gas, which we can measure with a mass balance, as shown. (The other method is to use a gas syringe, as above.)

These graphs show the effect of using stronger acid solutions

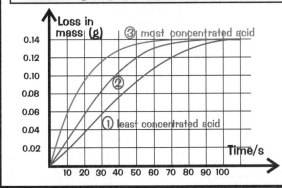

Loss in mass (g)

③ most concentrated acid

②

① least concentrated acid

Time/s

10 20 30 40 50 60 70 80 90 100

1) Take readings of the mass at regular time intervals.

2) Put the results in a table and work out the loss in mass for each reading. Plot a graph.

3) Repeat with stronger acid solutions but always with the same amount of magnesium.

4) The volume of acid must always be kept the same too — only the concentration is increased.

5) The three graphs show the same old pattern — a higher concentration gives a steeper graph with the reaction finishing much quicker.

Section Six — Rates of Reaction

Four Experiments on Rate of Reaction 2

3) Sodium Thiosulphate and HCl produce a Cloudy Precipitate

1) These two chemicals are both <u>clear solutions</u>.
2) They react together to form a <u>yellow precipitate</u> of <u>sulphur</u>.
3) <u>The experiment</u> involves watching a black mark <u>disappear</u> through the <u>cloudy sulphur</u> and <u>timing</u> how long it takes to go.

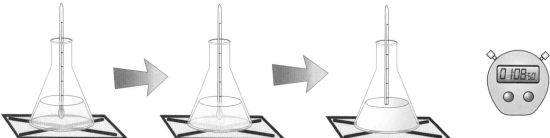

4) The reaction can be <u>repeated</u> for solutions at different <u>temperatures</u>.
5) The <u>depth</u> of liquid must be kept the <u>same</u> each time, of course.
6) The results will of course show that the <u>higher the temperature</u> the <u>quicker the reaction</u> and therefore the <u>less time</u> it takes for the mark to <u>disappear</u>.   These are typical results:

Temperature	20°C	25°C	30°C	35°C	40°C
Time taken for mark to disappear	193s	151s	112s	87s	52s

This reaction can <u>also</u> be used to test the effects of <u>concentration</u>.
   One sad thing about this reaction is <u>it doesn't give a set of graphs</u>. Well I think it's sad. All you get is a set of <u>readings</u> of how long it took till the mark disappeared for each temperature. Boring.

4) The Decomposition of Hydrogen Peroxide

This is a <u>good</u> reaction for showing the effect of different <u>catalysts</u>.
The decomposition of hydrogen peroxide is:

$$2H_2O_2 \rightleftharpoons 2H_2O + O_2$$

1) This is normally <u>quite slow</u> but a sprinkle of <u>manganese(IV) oxide catalyst</u> speeds it up no end. Other catalysts which work are
a) <u>potato peel</u> and b) <u>blood</u>.
2) <u>Oxygen gas</u> is given off, which provides an <u>ideal way</u> to measure the rate of reaction using the good ol' <u>gas syringe</u> method.

O₂ gas

Hydrogen peroxide

Catalyst

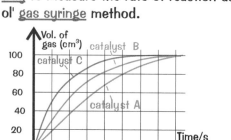

1) Same old graphs of course.
2) <u>Better catalysts</u> give a <u>quicker reaction</u> which is shown by a <u>steeper graph</u> which levels off quickly.
3) This reaction can also be used to measure the effects of <u>temperature</u>, or of <u>concentration</u> of the H_2O_2 solution. The graphs will look <u>just the same</u>.

Four Top Rate Reactions — learn and enjoy...

There's always so much happening with reaction rates. Is it products or reactants we're looking at? Are we measuring gas, or mass, or cloudiness? Is it the effect of temp. or conc. or catalyst or surface area we're investigating? There's just so much going on, <u>but you'll just have to sort it all out and learn it</u>.

Catalysts

Many reactions can be speeded up by adding a catalyst.

> A **CATALYST** is a substance which **INCREASES** the speed of a reaction, without being **CHANGED** or **USED UP** in the reaction.

1) Catalysts lower the Activation Energy

1) Catalysts lower the activation energy of reactions, making it easier for them to happen.
2) This means a lower temperature can be used.

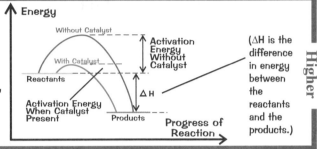

Higher

(ΔH is the difference in energy between the reactants and the products.)

2) Catalysts work best when they have a Big Surface Area

1) Catalysts are usually used as a powder or pellets or a fine gauze.
2) This gives them maximum surface area to enable the reacting particles to meet up and do the business.

Catalyst Powder   Catalyst Pellets   Catalyst Gauzes

3) Catalysts Help Reduce Costs in Industrial Reactions

1) Catalysts increase the rate of many industrial reactions, which saves a lot of money simply because the plant doesn't need to operate for as long to produce the same amount of stuff.
2) Alternatively, a catalyst will allow the reaction to work at a much lower temperature and that can save a lot of money too. Catalysts are therefore very important for commercial reasons.
3) Catalysts are used over and over again.   They may need cleaning but they don't get used up.
4) Different reactions use different catalysts.
5) Transition metals are common catalysts in many industrial reactions. Know these two:

a) An Iron Catalyst is used in the Haber Process

$$N_{2\,(g)} \; + \; 3H_{2\,(g)} \; \xrightarrow{\text{Iron Catalyst}} \; 2NH_{3\,(g)}$$

b) A Platinum Catalyst is used in the production of Nitric Acid (See P. 55)

$$\text{Ammonia} \; + \; \text{Oxygen} \; \xrightarrow{\text{Platinum Catalyst}} \; \text{Nitrogen monoxide} \; + \; \text{Water}$$

4) Catalytic Converters in Cars contain Platinum

1) Catalytic converters are fitted in the exhaust system of all new cars.
2) Normal exhaust gases include unburnt petrol, carbon monoxide and oxides of nitrogen.
3) The catalytic converters cause a reaction between these badly polluting exhaust gases to produce harmless gases: — nitrogen, oxygen, carbon dioxide and water vapour.

Catalysts are like great jokes — you can use them over and over...

Make sure you learn the definition in the top box word for word. The fact is they can easily ask you: "What is a catalyst?" (2 Marks).   This is much easier to answer if you have a "word for word" definition at the ready. If you don't, you're likely to lose half the marks on it. That's a fact.

Enzymes

Enzymes seem to crop up in all sorts of places in chemistry. That's because they're great.

Enzymes are Biological Catalysts

1) <u>Living things</u> have thousands of different chemical processes going on inside them.

2) The <u>quicker</u> these happen the <u>better</u>, and having a <u>warm</u> body is an important way to <u>speed them up</u>.

3) However, there's a <u>limit</u> to how far you can <u>raise</u> the temperature before <u>cells</u> start getting <u>damaged</u>, so living things also produce <u>enzymes</u> which act as <u>catalysts</u> to <u>speed up</u> all these chemical reactions without the need for <u>high temperatures</u>.

Enzymes are produced by Living Things — and they're Ace

1) Every <u>different</u> biological process has its <u>own enzyme</u> designed especially for it.

2) Enzymes have <u>two main advantages</u> over <u>non-organic</u> catalysts:
    a) They're <u>not scarce</u> like many metal catalysts eg. platinum.
    b) They work best at <u>low temperatures</u>, which keeps <u>costs down</u>.

Enzymes Like it Warm but Not Too Hot

1) The chemical reactions in <u>living cells</u> are quite fast in conditions that are <u>warm</u> rather than <u>hot</u>.

2) This is because the cells use <u>enzyme</u> catalysts, which are <u>protein molecules</u>.

3) Enzymes are usually <u>damaged</u> by temperatures above about <u>45°C</u>, and as the graph shows, their activity drops off <u>sharply</u> when the temperature gets <u>a little too high</u>.

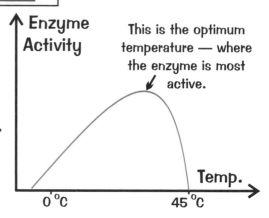

This is the optimum temperature — where the enzyme is most active.

Enzymes Like the right pH too

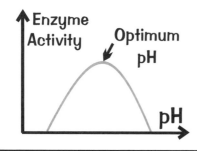

1) The <u>pH</u> affects the activity of enzymes, in a similar way to temperature.

2) The graph shows how the enzyme activity reaches a <u>peak</u> at a certain pH. If the pH is above or below this optimum level, the enzyme activity <u>falls</u>.

3) <u>Different</u> enzymes have <u>different</u> optimum pH levels.

"Enzymes" — sounds like a brand of throat lozenge...

Enzymes are like my cat — they're pretty fussy about just about everything. Not only do they like the temperature to be just right — the pH has to be pretty much spot on as well.
This page is definitely a candidate for the mini-essay method. Two mini-essays in fact.
What else is there to say? <u>Scribble down the facts, then look back and see what you missed.</u>

Uses of Enzymes

Living cells use chemical reactions to produce many new products which are useful to us.

Yeast in Brewing of Beer and Wine: Fermentation

1) Yeast cells convert sugar into carbon dioxide and alcohol.
2) They do this using the enzyme ZYMASE.
3) The main thing is to keep the temperature just right. If it's too cold the enzyme won't work very quickly. If it's too hot it will destroy the enzyme.
4) This biological process is called fermentation and is used for making alcoholic drinks like beer and wine.

> FERMENTATION is the process of yeast converting sugar into carbon dioxide and alcohol.
>
> Glucose $\xrightarrow{\text{Zymase}}$ Carbon dioxide + Ethanol (+ Energy)

Yeast in Bread-making: Fermentation again

1) The reaction in bread-making is exactly the same as that in brewing.
2) Yeast cells use the enzyme zymase to break down sugar and this gives them energy.
3) It also releases carbon dioxide gas and alcohol as waste products.
4) The carbon dioxide gas is produced throughout the bread mixture and forms in bubbles everywhere.
5) This makes the bread rise and gives it its familiar texture. The small amount of alcohol also gives the bread some extra flavour, no doubt.
6) When the bread is put in the oven the yeast is killed and the reaction stops.

Yoghurt and Cheese making — only pasteurised milk

1) Pasteurised milk MUST be used for making cheese and yoghurt, because fresh milk contains many unwanted bacteria which would give them a bad taste.
2) The pasteurised milk is mixed with specially grown cultures of bacteria.
3) This mixture is kept at the ideal temperature for the bacteria and their enzymes to work.
4) For yoghurt this is pretty warm at about 45°C.
5) The yoghurt-making bacteria convert lactose (the natural sugar found in milk), into lactic acid. This gives yoghurts their slightly bitter taste.
6) Cheese on the other hand matures better in cooler conditions.
7) Various bacterial enzymes can be used in cheese making to produce different textures and tastes.

Enzymes have a load of other uses...

1) The proteins in some baby foods are 'pre-digested' using protein-digesting enzymes (proteases).
2) The centres of chocolates can be softened using enzymes.
3) Enzymes can turn starch syrup (yuk) into sugar syrup (yum).
4) Glucose syrup can be turned into fructose syrup. Fructose is sweeter, so you need less of it.
5) Enzymes are the 'biological' ingredients in biological washing powder. They're mainly protein-digesting enzymes (proteases) and fat-digesting enzymes (lipases) so they're ideal for removing food stains.

This page is just so easy — it's a blummin' picnic...

This is rapidly turning into a Domestic Science book. Anyway, you need to know how they make bread, wine, cheese, yoghurt, weird sugars, baby food and washing powder. Mini-essays again, I'd say. Enjoy.

Revision Summary for Section Six

I suppose some of the stuff on Rates of Reaction gets a bit chewy in places, but the rest is all a bit of a breeze really, isn't it? Anyway, here's some more of those nice easy questions which you enjoy so much. Remember, if you can't answer one, look at the appropriate page and learn the facts. Then go back and try all the questions again. Your hope is that one day you'll be able to glide effortlessly through all of them — it's a nice trick if you can do it.

1) What are the three different ways of measuring the speed of a reaction?

2) What are the four factors which the rate of reaction depends on?

3) Explain how each of these four factors increase the *number of collisions* between particles.

4) What is the other aspect of collision theory which determines the rate of reaction?

5) Which is the only physical factor which affects this other aspect of the collisions?

6) What happens when hydrochloric acid is added to marble chips?

7) Give details of the two possible methods for measuring the rate of this reaction.

8) Sketch a typical set of graphs for either of these methods.

9) Describe in detail how you would test the effect on the reaction rate of
     a) finer particles of solid   b) stronger concentration of acid   c) temperature

10) What happens when sodium thiosulphate is added to HCl? How is the rate measured?

11) Write down the equation for the decomposition of hydrogen peroxide.

12) What is the best way to increase the rate of this reaction?

13) What is the best way to measure the rate of this reaction? What will the graphs look like?

14) What is the definition of a catalyst? What does a catalyst do to the activation energy?

15) Name two specific industrial catalysts and the processes they are used in.

16) What are enzymes?

17) Give two advantages of enzymes over non-biological catalysts.

18) Sketch the graph for enzyme activity vs temperature, indicating the temperatures.

19) Give three examples of the use of enzymes by people.

20) Give the word-equation for fermentation. Which organism and which enzyme are involved?

21) Explain what happens in brewing and bread-making. What is the difference between them?

22) What kind of milk is needed for making cheese and yoghurt and why?

23) What gives yoghurt and cheese their flavour?

24) Explain how biological washing powders work.

Current, Voltage and Resistance

Isn't electricity great. Mind you it's pretty bad news if the words don't mean anything to you...

Learn these Basic Definitions before you Start...

1) _CURRENT_ is the flow of electrons round the circuit.
2) _VOLTAGE_ is the driving force that pushes the current round. Kind of like "electrical pressure".
3) _RESISTANCE_ is anything in the circuit which slows the flow down.
4) **THERE'S A** _BALANCE_: the voltage is trying to push the current round the circuit, and the resistance is opposing it — the relative sizes of the voltage and resistance decide how big the current will be:

> If you increase the _VOLTAGE_ — then _MORE CURRENT_ will flow.
> If you increase the _RESISTANCE_ — then _LESS CURRENT_ will flow.

Here are the All-Important Formulas...

If you don't learn anything else in this section, learn these formulas:

Quantity	Symbol	Units	Formula
Potential Difference	V	Volts, V	$V = I \times R$
Current	I	Amperes, A	$I = V / R$
Resistance	R	Ohms, Ω	$R = V / I$

Current is Just Like the Flow of Water Around a Set of Pipes

1) The current is simply like the flow of water.
2) Voltage is like the pressure provided by a pump which pushes the stuff round.
3) Resistance is any sort of constriction in the flow, which is what the pressure has to work against.
4) If you turn up the pump and provide more pressure (or "voltage"), the flow will increase.
5) If you put in more constrictions ("resistance"), the flow (current) will decrease.

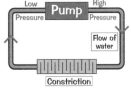

In Metals the Current is Carried by Electrons

1) Electric current will only flow if there are charges which can move freely.
2) Metals contain a "sea" of free electrons (which are negatively charged) and which flow throughout the metal.
3) This is what allows electric current to flow so well in all metals.

Energy is Transferred from Cells and Other Sources

1) Anything which supplies electricity is also supplying energy. There are four sources you need to learn:
   CELLS, BATTERIES, GENERATORS, SOLAR CELLS.
2) The energy is transferred by the electric circuit to components such as lamps, resistors, bells, motors, LEDs, buzzers, etc.
3) These components perform their own energy transfer and convert the electrical energy in the circuit into other forms of energy: HEAT, LIGHT, SOUND or MOVEMENT.

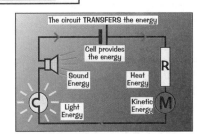

Note — all resistors produce heat when a current flows through them.

Understanding currents — easy as pie...

This page is all about electric current — what it is, what makes it move, and what tries to stop it. This is the most basic stuff on electricity there is. You realise that you'll never be able to learn anything else about electricity until you know this stuff — don't you? Just checking.

The Standard Test Circuit

This is without doubt the most totally bog-standard circuit the world has ever known. So know it.

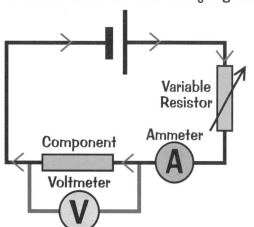

Variable Resistor

Component

Ammeter

Voltmeter

The Ammeter

1) Measures the <u>current</u> (in <u>Amps</u>) flowing through the component.
2) Must be placed <u>in series</u>.
3) Can be put <u>anywhere</u> in series in the <u>main circuit</u>, but never <u>in parallel</u> like the voltmeter.

The Voltmeter

1) Measures the <u>voltage</u> (in <u>Volts</u>) across the component.
2) Must be placed <u>in parallel</u> around the <u>component under test</u> — <u>NOT</u> around the variable resistor or the battery!
3) The <u>proper</u> name for "<u>voltage</u>" is "<u>potential difference</u>" or "<u>p.d.</u>"

Five Important Points

1) This <u>very basic circuit</u> is used for <u>testing components</u>, and for getting <u>V-I graphs</u> for them.
2) The <u>component</u>, the <u>ammeter</u> and the <u>variable resistor</u> are all <u>in series</u>, which means they can be put <u>in any order</u> in the main circuit. The <u>voltmeter</u>, on the other hand, can only be placed <u>in parallel</u> around the <u>component under test</u>, as shown. Anywhere else is a definite <u>no-no</u>.
3) As you <u>vary</u> the <u>variable resistor</u> it alters the <u>current</u> flowing through the circuit.
4) This allows you to take several <u>pairs of readings</u> from the <u>ammeter</u> and <u>voltmeter</u>.
5) You can then <u>plot</u> these values for <u>current</u> and <u>voltage</u> on a <u>V-I graph</u>, like the ones below.

Four Hideously Important Voltage-Current Graphs

V-I graphs show how the current varies as you change the voltage. Learn these four real well:

Resistor

Different Wires

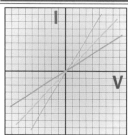

Filament Lamp

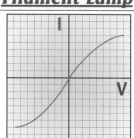

Diode

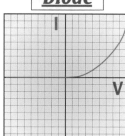

The current through a <u>resistor</u> (at constant temperature) is <u>proportional to voltage</u>.

<u>Different wires</u> have different <u>resistances</u>, hence the different <u>slopes</u>.

As the <u>temperature</u> of the filament <u>increases</u>, the <u>resistance increases</u>, hence the <u>curve</u>.

Current will only flow through a diode <u>in one direction</u>, as shown.

Calculating Resistance: R =V/I, (or R ="1/gradient")

For the <u>straight-line graphs</u> the resistance of the component is <u>steady</u> and is equal to the <u>inverse</u> of the <u>gradient</u> of the line, or "<u>1/gradient</u>". In other words, the <u>steeper</u> the graph, the <u>lower</u> the resistance. If the graph <u>curves</u>, it means the resistance is <u>changing</u>. In that case R can be found for any point by taking the <u>pair of values</u> (V, I) from the graph and sticking them in the formula <u>R =V/I</u> (See P.79). Easy.

In the end, you'll have to learn this — resistance is futile...

There are quite a lot of important details on this page and you need to <u>learn all of them</u>. The only way to make sure you really know it is to <u>cover up the page</u> and see how much of it you can <u>scribble down</u> from <u>memory</u>. Sure, it's not that easy — but it's the only way. Enjoy.

Circuit Symbols and Devices

You have to know <u>all</u> these circuit symbols for the Exam.

Circuit Symbols You Should Know:

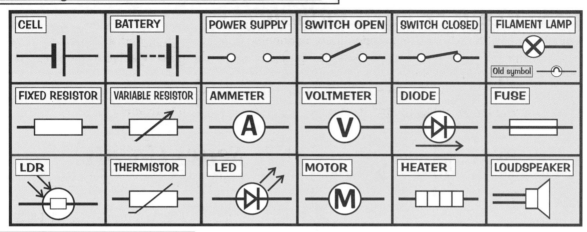

1) Variable Resistor

1) A <u>resistor</u> whose resistance can be <u>changed</u> by twiddling a knob or something.
2) The old-fashioned ones are <u>huge coils of wire</u> with a <u>slider</u> on them.
3) They're great for <u>altering the current</u> flowing through a circuit.
   Turn the resistance <u>up</u>, the current <u>drops</u>. Turn the resistance <u>down</u>, the current goes <u>up</u>.

2) "Semiconductor Diode" or just "Diode"

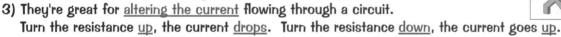

A special device made from <u>semiconductor</u> material such as <u>silicon</u>. It lets current flow freely through it <u>in one direction</u>, but <u>not</u> in the other (i.e. there's a very high resistance in the <u>reverse</u> direction). This turns out to be real useful in various <u>electronic circuits</u>.

3) Light Emitting Diode or "LED" to you

1) A diode which <u>gives out light</u>. It only lets current go through in <u>one direction</u>.
2) When it does pass current, it gives out a pretty <u>red</u> or <u>green</u> or <u>yellow</u> light.
3) Stereos usually have lots of jolly little LEDs which <u>light up</u> as the music's playing.

4) Light Dependent Resistor or "LDR" to you

1) In <u>bright light</u>, the resistance <u>falls</u>.
2) In <u>darkness</u>, the resistance is <u>highest</u>.
3) This makes it a useful device for various <u>electronic circuits</u> — e.g. <u>automatic night lights</u>, <u>burglar detectors</u>.

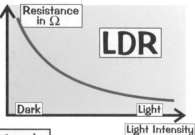

5) Thermistor (Temperature-dependent Resistor)

1) In <u>hot</u> conditions, the resistance <u>drops</u>.
2) In <u>cool</u> conditions, the resistance goes <u>up</u>.
3) Thermistors make useful <u>temperature detectors</u>. e.g. <u>car engine</u> temperature sensors and electronic <u>thermostats</u> for central heating.

   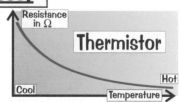

"Diode" — wasn't that a film starring Bruce Willis...

Another page of basic but important details about electrical circuits. You need to know all those circuit symbols as well as the extra details for the five special devices. When you think you know it all try <u>covering the page</u> and <u>scribbling it all down</u>. See how you did, and <u>then try again</u>.

Series Circuits

You need to be able to tell the difference between series and parallel circuits just by looking at them. You also need to know the rules about what happens with both types. Read on.

Series Circuits — all or nothing

1) In series circuits, the different components are connected in a line, end to end, between the +ve and −ve of the power supply (except for voltmeters, which are always connected in parallel, but they don't count as part of the circuit).
2) If you remove or disconnect one component, the circuit is broken and they all stop.
3) This is generally not very handy, and in practice, very few things are connected in series.

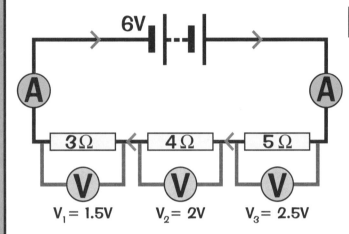

Voltages add to equal the supply: 1.5 + 2 + 2.5 = 6 V
Total resistance = 3 + 4 + 5 = 12 Ohms
Current = V/R = 6 / 12 = 0.5 A

In Series Circuits:

1) The total resistance is just the sum of all the resistances.
2) The same current flows through all parts of the circuit.
3) The size of the current is determined by the total p.d. of the cells and the total resistance of the circuit: i.e. $I = V/R$
4) The total p.d. of the supply is shared between the various components, so the voltages round a series circuit always add up to equal the total voltage of the supply.
5) The bigger the resistance of a component, the bigger its share of the total p.d.

Total p.d., Voltmeters and Ammeters

1) The total p.d. provided by cells in series is the sum of every individual p.d.
2) Voltmeters are always connected in parallel around components.
   In a series circuit, you can put voltmeters around each component. The readings from all the components will add up to equal the reading from the voltage source (the cells). Simple.
3) Ammeters can be placed anywhere in a series circuit and will all give the same reading.

Christmas Fairy Lights are Wired in Series

Christmas fairy lights are about the only real-life example of things connected in series, and we all know what a pain they are when the whole lot go out just because one of the bulbs is slightly dodgy.

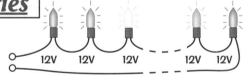

The only advantage is that the bulbs can be very small because the total 230V is shared out between them, so each bulb only has a small voltage across it.

By contrast, a string of lights as used on a building site are connected in parallel so that each bulb receives the full 230 V. If one is removed, the rest stay lit. Which is most convenient.

Make sure you know the difference between these two wiring diagrams.

Series Circuits — phew, it's just one thing after another...

They really do want you to know the difference between series and parallel circuits.
It's not that tricky but you do have to make a real effort to learn all the details. That's what this page is for. Learn all those details, then cover the page and scribble them all down. Then try again...

Parallel Circuits

Parallel circuits are much more sensible than series circuits and so they're much more common in real life.

Parallel Circuits — Independence and Isolation

1) In parallel circuits, each component is separately connected to the +ve and −ve of the supply.
2) If you remove or disconnect one of them, it will hardly affect the others at all.
3) This is obviously how most things must be connected, for example in cars and in household electrics. You have to be able to switch everything on and off separately.

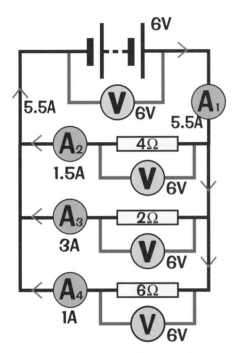

In Parallel Circuits:

1) All components get the full source p.d., so the voltage is the same across all components.

2) The current through each component depends on its resistance.
The lower the resistance, the bigger the current that'll flow through it.

3) The total current flowing around the circuit is equal to the total of all the currents in the separate branches.

4) In a parallel circuit, there are junctions where the current either splits or rejoins. The total current going into a junction always equals the total currents leaving — fairly obviously.

5) The total resistance of the circuit is tricky to work out, but it's always less than the branch with the smallest resistance.

Voltages all equal to supply voltage: = 6 V
Total R is less than the smallest, i.e. less than 2 W
Total Current (A₁) = sum of all branches = A₂+A₃+A₄

Connection of Voltmeters and Ammeters

1) Once again the voltmeters are always connected in parallel around components.

2) Ammeters can be placed in each branch to measure the different currents flowing through each branch, as well as one near the supply to measure the total current flowing out of it.

Everything Electrical in a Car is Connected in Parallel

Parallel connection is essential in a car to give these two features:

1) Everything can be turned on and off separately.
2) Everything always gets the full voltage from the battery.

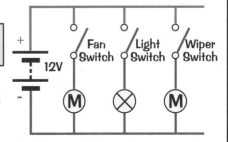

The only slight effect is that when you turn lots of things on the lights may go dim because the battery can't provide full voltage under heavy load. This is normally a very slight effect. You can spot the same thing at home when you turn a kettle on, if you watch very carefully.

Electric Circuits — unparalleled dreariness...

Make sure you can scribble down a parallel circuit and know what the advantages are. Learn the numbered points and the details for connecting ammeters and voltmeters, and also what two features make parallel connection essential in a car. Then cover the page and scribble it...

The Cost of Domestic Electricity

Electricity is by far the <u>most useful</u> form of energy. Compared to gas or oil or coal etc. it's <u>much easier</u> to turn it into the <u>four main types</u> of useful energy: <u>Heat</u>, <u>light</u>, <u>sound</u> and <u>motion</u>.

Reading Your Electricity Meter and Working out the Bill

Yip, this is in the syllabus. Don't ask me why, because you never actually need to bother in real life.

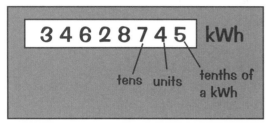

tens   units   tenths of a kWh

The reading on your meter shows the <u>total number of units</u> (kWh) used since the meter was fitted. Each bill is worked out from the <u>increase</u> in the meter reading since it was <u>last read</u> for the previous bill.

You need to <u>study</u> this bill until you know what all the different bits <u>are for</u>, and how it all works out. They could give you one <u>very similar</u> in the Exam.

Electricity Bill

Previous meter reading............345412.3	
This meter reading...................346287.5	
Number of units used.......................875.2	
Cost per unit.......................................6.3p	
Cost of electricity used...................£55.14	
(875.2 units × 6.3p)	
Fixed Quarterly charge.....................£7.50	
Total Bill..£62.64	
VAT @ 8%...£5.01	
Final total..**£67.65**	

Kilowatt-hours (kWh) are "UNITS" of Energy

1) Your electricity meter counts the number of "<u>UNITS</u>" used.
2) A "<u>UNIT</u>" is otherwise known as a <u>kilowatt-hour</u>, or <u>kWh</u>.
3) A "<u>kWh</u>" might sound like a unit of power, but it's not — it's an <u>amount of energy</u>.

> A <u>**KILOWATT-HOUR**</u> is the amount of electrical energy used by a <u>1 kW appliance</u> left on for <u>1 HOUR</u>.

4) Make sure you can turn <u>1 kWh</u> into <u>3,600,000 Joules</u> like this:
"E=P×t" = 1 kW × 1 hour = 1000 W × 3,600 secs = <u>3,600,000 J</u>   (=3.6 MJ)
(The formula is "Energy = power×time", and the units must be converted to <u>watts</u> and <u>seconds</u> first.

The Two Easy Formulas for Calculating The Cost of Electricity

These must surely be the two most <u>trivial and obvious</u> formulas you'll ever see:

No. of <u>UNITS</u> (kWh) used = <u>POWER</u> (in kW) × <u>TIME</u> (in hours)	Units = kW × hours
<u>COST</u> = No. of <u>UNITS</u> × <u>PRICE</u> per UNIT	Cost = Units × Price

<u>EXAMPLE</u>: *Find the cost of leaving a 60 W light bulb on for a) 30 minutes   b) one year.*
<u>ANSWER</u>: a) <u>No. of Units = kW × hours</u> = 0.06 kW × ½hr = 0.03 units.
       <u>Cost = Units × price per unit</u>(6.3p) = 0.03 × 6.3p = <u>0.189p</u> for 30 mins.

     b) <u>No. of Units = kW × hours</u> = 0.06 kW × (24×365) hr = 525.6 units.
       <u>Cost = Units × price per unit</u>(6.3p) = 525.6 × 6.3p = <u>£33.11</u> for one year.

N.B.   Always turn the <u>power</u> into <u>kW</u> (not Watts) and the <u>time</u> into <u>hours</u> (not minutes)

Kilowa Towers — the best lit hotel in Hawaii...

This page has three sections and you need to learn the stuff in all of them. Start by memorising the headings, then learn the details under each heading. Then <u>cover the page</u> and <u>scribble down</u> what you know. Check back and see what you missed, and then <u>try again</u>. And keep trying.

Mains Electricity — Plugs and Fuses

Now then, did you know... electricity is dangerous. It can kill you. Well just watch out for it, that's all.

Hazards in the Home — Eliminate Them before They Eliminate You

A <u>likely Exam question</u> will show you a picture of domestic bliss but with various <u>electrical hazards</u> in the picture such as kids shoving their fingers into sockets and stuff like that, and they'll ask you to <u>list all the hazards</u>. This should be mostly <u>common sense</u>, but it won't half help if you've already learnt this list:

1) <u>Long cables</u> or <u>frayed cables</u>.
2) <u>Cables</u> in contact with something <u>hot</u> or <u>wet</u>.
3) Pet rabbits or <u>children</u> (always hazardous).
4) <u>Water near sockets</u>, or <u>shoving</u> things into sockets.
5) <u>Damaged plugs</u>, or <u>too many</u> plugs into one socket.
6) Lighting sockets <u>without bulbs in</u>.
7) Appliances without their <u>covers</u> on.

Plugs and Cables — Learn the Safety Features

Get the Wiring Right:

1) The <u>right coloured wire</u> is connected to each pin, and <u>firmly screwed</u> in.

2) <u>No bare wires</u> showing inside the plug.

3) <u>Cable grip</u> tightly fastened over the cable <u>outer layer</u>.

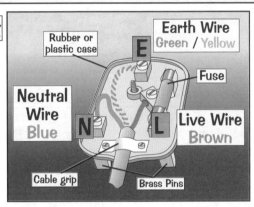

Rubber or plastic case

Earth Wire Green / Yellow

E

Fuse

Neutral Wire Blue

N   L

Live Wire Brown

Cable grip

Brass Pins

Plug Features:

1) The <u>metal parts</u> are made of copper or brass because these are <u>very good conductors</u>.
2) The case, cable grip and cable insulation are all made of <u>plastic</u> because this is a really good <u>insulator</u> and is <u>flexible</u> too.
3) This all keeps the electricity flowing <u>where it should</u>.

Earthing and Fuses Prevent Fires and Shocks

The <u>LIVE WIRE</u> alternates between a <u>HIGH +VE AND −VE VOLTAGE</u>, with an average of about <u>230 V</u>. The <u>NEUTRAL WIRE</u> is always at <u>0 V</u>. Electricity normally flows in and out through the live and neutral wires only. The <u>EARTH WIRE</u> and <u>fuse</u> (or circuit breaker) are just for <u>safety</u> and <u>work together</u> like this:

1) If a <u>fault</u> develops in which the <u>live</u> somehow touches the <u>metal case</u>, then because the case is <u>earthed</u>, a <u>big current</u> flows in through the <u>live</u>, through the <u>case</u> and out down the <u>earth wire</u>.

2) This <u>surge</u> in current <u>blows the fuse</u> (or trips the circuit breaker), which <u>cuts off</u> the <u>live supply</u>.

3) This <u>isolates</u> the <u>whole appliance</u> making it <u>impossible</u> to get an electric <u>shock</u> from the case. It also prevents the risk of <u>fire</u> caused by the heating effect of a large current.

4) <u>Fuses</u> should be <u>rated</u> as near as possible but <u>just higher</u> than the <u>normal operating current</u> (See P. 86).

TOASTER   heater coil

Big current surges to earth

Big current now flows out through earth

Fault Allows live to touch metal case

Big surge in current blows fuse......

....which isolates the appliance from the live

pop

Safe

All appliances with <u>metal cases</u> must be "<u>earthed</u>" to avoid the danger of <u>electric shock</u>. "Earthing" just means the metal case must be <u>attached to the earth wire</u> in the cable. If the appliance has a <u>plastic casing</u> and no metal parts <u>showing</u> then it's said to be <u>double insulated</u>. Anything with <u>double insulation</u> like that <u>doesn't need an earth wire</u>, just a live and neutral.

Some people are so careless with electricity — it's shocking...

Make sure you can list all those hazards in the home. Make sure you know all the details for wiring a plug. Trickiest of all, make sure you understand how earthing and fuses act together to make things safe. Learnt it all? Good-O. So <u>cover the page</u> and <u>scribble it all down again</u>.

The National Grid

1) The National Grid is the network of pylons and cables which covers the whole country.
2) It takes electricity from the power stations, to just where it's needed in homes and industry.
3) It enables power to be generated anywhere on the grid, and then supplied anywhere else on the grid.

All Power Stations are Pretty Much the Same

They all have a boiler of some sort, which makes steam which drives a turbine which drives a generator. The generator produces electricity (by induction) by rotating an electromagnet within coils of wire.

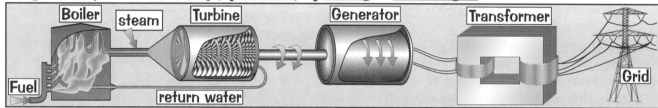

Learn all these features of the NATIONAL GRID — power stations, transformers, pylons, etc:

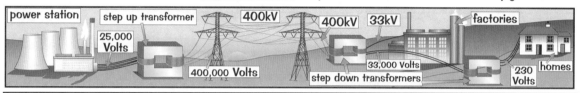

Pylon Cables are at 400,000 V to keep the Current Low

You need to understand why the voltage is so high and why it's AC. Learn these points:
1) The formula for power supplied is: Power = Voltage × Current or: P = V×I
2) So to transmit a lot of power, you either need high voltage or high current.
3) The problem with high current is the loss (as heat) due to the resistance of the cables.
4) The formula for power loss due to resistance in the cables is: $P = I^2R$.
5) Because of the I^2 bit, if the current is 10 times bigger, the losses will be 100 times bigger.
6) It's much cheaper to boost the voltage up to 400,000 V and keep the current very low.
7) This requires transformers as well as big pylons with huge insulators, but it's still cheaper.
8) The transformers have to step the voltage up at one end, for efficient transmission, and then bring it back down to safe useable levels at the other end.
9) This is why it has to be AC on the National Grid — transformers only work with AC.
10) Mains electricity in your house is AC 50 Hz — the voltage changes direction 100 times a second.

Calculating Electrical Power and Fuse Ratings

1) The standard formula for electrical power is: $P=VI$
2) If you combine it with V=I×R, and replace the "V" with "I×R", you get: $P=I^2R$
3) If instead you use V=I×R and replace the "I" with "V/R", you get: $P=V^2/R$
4) You choose which one of these formulas to use, purely and simply by seeing which one contains the three quantities which are involved in the problem you're looking at.

Calculating Fuse Ratings — Always Use the Formula: "P=VI"

Most electrical goods indicate their power rating and voltage rating. To work out the fuse needed, you need to work out the current that the item will normally use. That means using "P=VI", or rather, "I=P/V".
EXAMPLE: A hairdrier is rated at 240V, 1.1 kW. Find the fuse needed.
ANSWER: I = P/V = 1100/240 = 4.6 A. Normally, the fuse should be rated just a little higher than the normal current, so a 5 amp fuse is ideal for this one.

400,000 Volts? — that could give you a buzz...

Quite a few tricky details on this page. The power station and National Grid are easy enough, but fully explaining why pylon cables are at 400,000 V is a bit trickier — but you do need to learn it. The same goes for the power formulas and working out fuse ratings. Scribble it.

Revision Summary for Section Seven

Electricity. What fun. This is definitely Physics at its most grisly. The big problem with Physics in general is that usually there's nothing to "see". You're told that there's a current flowing, but there's nothing you can actually see with your eyes. That's what makes it so difficult. To get to grips with Physics you have to get used to learning about things which you can't see. Try these questions and see how well you're doing.

1) Write down definitions for current, voltage and resistance. Explain how the three are related.

2) What happens to the current in a circuit when you increase the voltage? What about when you increase the resistance?

3) Write down formulas for voltage, current and resistance (in terms of the other two quantities).

4) What carries current in metals? Explain why metals are able to conduct electricity.

5) What are the four types of energy that electricity can easily be converted into?

6) Sketch a circuit showing four devices converting energy. Describe all the energy changes.

7) Sketch out the standard test circuit with all the details. Describe how it's used.

8) Sketch the four standard V-I graphs and explain their shapes. How do you get R from them?

9) Scribble down 18 circuit symbols that you know, with their names of course.

10) Write down two facts about: a) variable resistors b) diodes c) LEDs d) LDRs
e) thermistors.

11) Sketch a typical series circuit and say why it is a series circuit, not a parallel one.

12) State five rules about the current, voltage and resistance in a series circuit.

13) Give examples of lights wired in series and wired in parallel and explain the main differences.

14) Sketch a typical parallel circuit, showing voltmeter and ammeter positions.

15) State five rules about the current, voltage and resistance in a parallel circuit.

16) Draw a circuit diagram of part of a car's electrics, and explain why they are in parallel.

17) Go and look at the electricity meter where you live and explain what the number on it represents.

18) What's a kilowatt-hour? What are the two easy formulas for finding the cost of electricity?

19) Name seven common electrical hazards in the home.

20) Sketch a properly wired plug. Explain fully how fuses work.

21) Describe what earthing and double insulation are. Why are they useful?

22) Sketch a typical power station and the national grid, and explain why the national grid is at 400 kV.

Waves — Basic Principles

Waves are different from anything else. You need to know in what ways.

Waves have various features which Only waves have

1) The AMPLITUDE goes from the middle line to the peak,
   NOT from a trough to a peak.
2) The WAVELENGTH (λ) covers a full cycle of the wave,
   e.g. from peak to peak.
3) FREQUENCY (f) is how many complete waves there are per second
   (passing a certain point). Frequency is measured in hertz (Hz).
   1 Hz is 1 complete wave per second.
4) The PERIOD (T) is the time taken for one complete wave. The formula is $T = 1/f$.

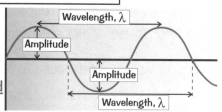

Transverse Waves have Sideways Vibrations

Most waves are transverse:
1) Light and all other EM waves.
2) Ripples on water.
3) Waves on strings.
4) A slinky spring wiggled up and down.

In TRANSVERSE waves the vibrations are at 90°
to the DIRECTION OF TRAVEL of the wave.

Vibrations from side to side | Wave travelling this way

Longitudinal Waves have Vibrations along the Same Line

The ONLY longitudinal waves are:
1) Sound waves.
2) A slinky spring when plucked.
3) Shock waves e.g. seismic P-waves in earthquakes.

In LONGITUDINAL waves the vibrations are along
the SAME DIRECTION as the wave is travelling.

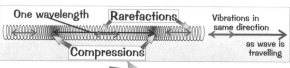

One wavelength | Rarefactions | Vibrations in same direction as wave is travelling
Compressions

Don't get confused by CRO displays which show a transverse wave
when displaying sounds. The real sound wave is longitudinal — the
display shows a transverse wave just so you can see what's going on.

Waves can be REFLECTED and REFRACTED and DIFFRACTED

More about these three beauties later — on pages 90-94.

Amplitude is a Measure of the Energy Carried by Any Wave

1) The greater the amplitude, the more energy
   the wave carries.
2) In sound this means it'll be louder.
3) Bigger amplitude means a louder sound.
4) With light, a bigger amplitude means it'll be
   brighter.

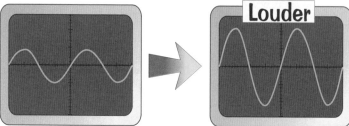

Louder

Learn about waves — just get into the vibes, man...

Once again the page is broken up into various sections with important numbered points for each.
All those numbered points are important. They're all mentioned specifically in the syllabuses so
you should expect them to test exactly this stuff in the Exams. Learn and enjoy.

Sound and Ultrasound

Sound travels as a Wave

1) Sound Waves are caused by vibrating objects.
2) Like all waves, sound waves can be reflected (i.e. echoes), refracted (as it passes into different media), and diffracted around obstacles (e.g. sound waves will diffract around doors — see page 94).
3) Sound waves are longitudinal waves, and travel at fixed speeds in particular media — the denser the medium, the faster sound travels through it.
4) This means sound generally travels faster in solids than in liquids, and faster in liquids than in gases.
5) But one thing sound waves can't do is travel through a vacuum.

The Frequency of a Sound Wave Determines its Pitch

1) High frequency sound waves sound high pitched like a squeaking mouse.
2) Low frequency sound waves sound low pitched like a mooing cow.
3) Frequency is the number of complete vibrations each second.
4) Common units are kHz (1000 Hz) and MHz (1,000,000 Hz).
5) High frequency (or high pitch) also means shorter wavelength.

| Original Sound | Higher pitched | Lower pitched | Higher pitched and louder |

Make sure you know all about these CRO traces.

Echoes and Reverberation are due to Sound Being REFLECTED

Sounds are reflected best from hard flat surfaces. Things like carpets and curtains act as absorbing surfaces which will absorb sounds rather than reflect them. This is why a big empty room sounds completely different once you've put carpet and curtains in — these things absorb the sound quickly and stop it echoing (reverberating) around the room.

Ultrasound is Sound with a Higher Frequency than We Can Hear

Electrical devices can be made which produce electrical oscillations of any frequency. These can easily be converted into mechanical vibrations to produce sound waves beyond the range of human hearing (i.e. frequencies above 20 kHz). This is called ultrasound and it has loads of uses:

Industrial Cleaning

Ultrasound is used to clean delicate mechanisms without them having to be dismantled. Ultrasound waves can be directed very precisely and are extremely good at removing deposits which form on delicate equipment. Other methods could cause damage or require the equipment to be dismantled.

And dentists use ultrasonic tools to remove tartar, which builds up on teeth and leads to gum disease.

Industrial Quality Control

Ultrasound waves can produce a visual display of the insides of objects. The waves can pass through something like a metal casting and whenever they reach a boundary between two different media (like metal and air) some of the wave is reflected back and detected.

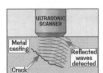

For Pre-Natal Scanning of a Foetus

This uses the same principle as industrial quality control. Ultrasound waves are reflected and processed to produce an image of the foetus. No one knows for sure whether ultrasound is safe in all cases but X-rays would definitely be dangerous to the foetus.

Amplitude — isn't that a word to say how "chubby" you are...

Another page with various sections. There does seem to be quite a lot of this stuff on boring ordinary waves and sound. But the simple truth is that the more of it you really learn properly, the more marks you'll get in the Exam. You do realise I hope that most Exam questions, even in Physics, simply test whether or not you've learned the basic facts. Just easy marks really.

Reflection: a Property of all Waves

The Ripple Tank is Really Good for Displaying Waves

Learn all these diagrams showing reflection of waves. They could ask you to complete any one of them in the Exam. It can be quite a bit trickier than you think unless you've practised them really well beforehand.

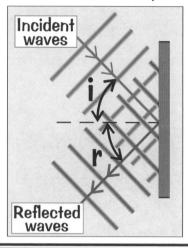

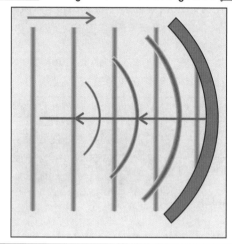

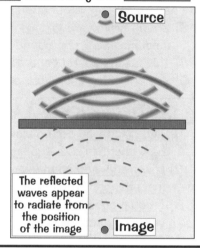

The reflected waves appear to radiate from the position of the image

Reflection of Light

1) Reflection of light is what allows us to see objects.
2) When light reflects from an uneven surface such as a piece of paper the light reflects off at all different angles and you get a DIFFUSE REFLECTION.
3) When light reflects from an even surface (smooth and shiny like a mirror) then it's all reflected at the same angle and you get a clear reflection.
4) But don't forget, the LAW OF REFLECTION applies to every reflected ray:

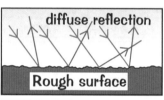

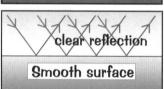

Angle of INCIDENCE = Angle of REFLECTION

Reflection in a Plane Mirror — How to Locate The Image

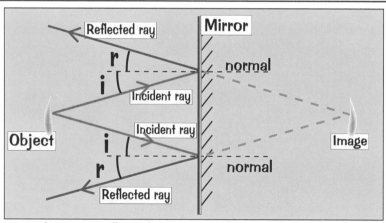

You need to be able to reproduce this entire diagram of how an image is formed in a PLANE MIRROR.
Learn these three important points:

1) The image is the same size as the object.
2) It is AS FAR BEHIND the mirror as the object is in front.
3) It's formed from diverging rays, which means it's a virtual image.

1) To draw any reflected ray, just make sure the angle of reflection, r, equals the angle of incidence, i.
2) Note that these two angles are ALWAYS defined between the ray itself and the dotted NORMAL.
3) Don't ever label them as the angle between the ray and the surface. Definitely uncool.

Learn reflection thoroughly — try to look at it from all sides...

First make sure you can draw all those diagrams from memory. Then make sure you've learnt the rest well enough to answer typical mean Exam questions like these: "Explain why you can see a piece of paper" "What is diffuse reflection?" "Why is the image in a plane mirror virtual?"

Refraction: a Property of all Waves

1) <u>Refraction</u> is when waves <u>change direction</u> as they <u>enter a different medium</u>.
2) This is caused <u>entirely</u> by the <u>change in speed</u> of the waves.
3) It also causes the <u>wavelength</u> to change, but remember that the <u>frequency</u> does <u>not</u> change.

1) Refraction is Shown by Waves in a Ripple Tank Slowing Down

1) The waves travel <u>slower</u> in <u>shallower water</u>, causing <u>refraction</u> as shown.
2) There's a <u>change in direction</u>, and a <u>change in wavelength</u> but <u>NO change in frequency</u>.

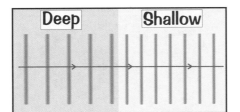

2) Refraction of Light — The Good Old Glass Block Demo

You can't fail to remember the old "<u>ray of light through a rectangular glass block</u>" trick.
Make sure you can draw this diagram <u>from memory</u>, with every detail <u>perfect</u>.

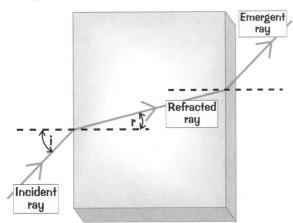

1) <u>Take careful note</u> of the positions of the <u>normals</u> and the <u>exact positions</u> of the angles of <u>incidence</u> and <u>refraction</u> (and note it's the angle of <u>refraction</u> — not <u>reflection</u>).
2) Most important of all, remember <u>which way</u> the ray <u>bends</u>.
3) The ray bends <u>towards the normal</u> as it enters the <u>denser medium</u>, and <u>away</u> from the normal as it <u>emerges</u> into the <u>less dense</u> medium.
4) Try to <u>visualise</u> the shape of the <u>wiggle</u> in the diagram — that can be easier than remembering the rule in words.

3) Refraction is always Caused by the Waves Changing Speed

1) When waves <u>slow down</u> they bend <u>towards</u> the normal.
2) When <u>light</u> enters <u>glass</u> it <u>slows down</u> to about <u>2/3</u> of its normal speed (in air) i.e. it slows down to about 2×10^8 m/s rather than 3×10^8 m/s.
3) When waves hit the boundary <u>along a normal</u>, i.e. at <u>exactly 90°</u>, then there will be <u>no change</u> in direction. That's pretty important to remember, because they often <u>sneak it into a question</u> somewhere. There'll still be a change in <u>speed</u> and <u>wavelength</u>, though.
4) <u>Some</u> light is also <u>reflected</u> when light hits a <u>different medium</u> such as glass.

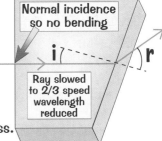

4) Sound Waves also Refract But it's Hard to Spot

<u>Sound waves</u> will also refract (change direction) as they enter <u>different media</u>. However, since sound waves are always <u>spreading out so much</u>, the change in direction is <u>hard to spot</u> under normal circumstances. (E.g. sound waves going from air to water bend <u>away</u> from the normal because, unlike light, they're <u>speeding up</u>.) *Just remember, sound waves do refract, OK?*

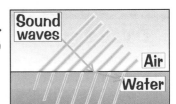

Revise Refraction — but don't let it slow you down...

The first thing you've gotta do is make sure you can spot the difference between the words *refraction* and *reflection*. After that you need to <u>learn all this stuff about refraction</u> — so you know exactly what it is. Make sure you know all those <u>diagrams</u> inside out. <u>Cover and scribble</u>.

92

Total Internal Reflection

Total Internal Reflection and The Critical Angle

1) This <u>only happens</u> when <u>light</u> is <u>coming out</u> of something <u>dense</u> like <u>glass</u> or <u>water</u> or <u>perspex</u>.
2) If the <u>angle</u> is <u>shallow enough</u> the ray <u>won't come out at all</u>, but it <u>reflects</u> back into the glass
(or whatever). This is called <u>total internal reflection</u> because <u>all</u> of the light <u>reflects back in</u>.

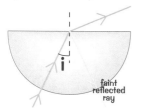 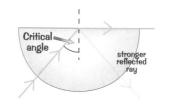 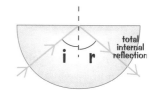

Angle of Incidence LESS than the Critical Angle.
Most light <u>passes through</u>, but a <u>little</u> is <u>internally reflected</u>.

Angle of Incidence EQUAL TO the Critical Angle.
The ray comes out <u>along the surface</u> — there's quite a bit of <u>internal reflection</u>.

Angle of Incidence GREATER than the Critical Angle.
<u>No light comes out</u> — it's <u>all</u> reflected, i.e. <u>total internal reflection</u>.

1) The <u>Critical Angle</u> for <u>glass</u> is about 42°. This is <u>very handy</u> because it means <u>45° angles</u> can be used to get <u>total internal reflection</u> as in the <u>prisms</u> in the <u>binoculars</u> and <u>periscope</u> shown below.
2) In *diamond* the <u>Critical Angle</u> is much <u>lower</u> — about <u>24°</u>. This is the reason why diamonds <u>sparkle</u> so much, because there are lots of <u>internal reflections</u>.

Uses of Total Internal Reflection

Binoculars, Periscopes and Bike Reflectors

In <u>binoculars</u> and <u>periscopes</u>, prisms give a <u>slightly better reflection</u> than a <u>mirror</u> would and they're also <u>easier</u> to hold accurately <u>in place</u>. Learn the <u>exact positioning</u> of the prisms.

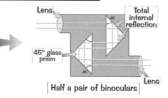 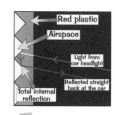

In <u>reflectors</u> prisms send the light back in <u>exactly the opposite direction</u> that it came from, so that whoever <u>shines the light</u> gets a <u>strong reflection</u> straight back at their eyes.

Optical Fibres

1) <u>Optical fibres</u> carry <u>information</u> by repeated <u>total internal reflections</u>. If the fibre's narrow enough, and isn't bent <u>too sharply</u> anywhere, the angle's always <u>above the critical angle</u>, and the signal gets bounced along the fibre.
2) They have <u>advantages</u> over <u>electrical signals</u> in wires:
   a) the same size cable can carry a lot <u>more information</u>.
   b) the signals don't suffer <u>interference</u> from electrical sources.
3) The signal still needs <u>boosting</u> every <u>few km</u>, as some light is <u>lost</u> due to <u>imperfections</u> in the surface.

 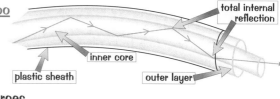

Endoscopes

An endoscope is a <u>narrow bunch</u> of <u>optical fibres</u> with a <u>lens system</u> at each end. Another bunch of optical fibres carries light down <u>inside</u> to see with. Endoscopes are used to do operations <u>without</u> cutting big holes in people. This was never possible before optical fibres.

Revision — sure it's Critical, but it's not a prism sentence...

First and foremost make sure you can <u>scribble all the diagrams</u> down with all the details. Then <u>scribble a mini-essay</u> for each topic, jotting down everything you can remember. Then check back and see what you <u>missed</u>. Then <u>learn the stuff you forgot</u> and <u>try again</u>. Ahh... such fun.

Section Eight — Waves and Outer Space

Digital and Analogue Signals

You've got to learn the two different ways of transmitting information.

Information is Converted into Signals

1) Information (e.g. sound, speech, pictures) is converted into electrical signals before it's transmitted.
2) It's then sent long distances down cables, like telephone calls or internet, or carried on EM waves, like radio or TV.

Analogue Varies but Digital's Either On or Off

1) The amplitude and frequency of analogue signals vary continuously like in sound waves. Parts of an analogue signal have any value in a range.
2) Dimmer switches, thermometers, speedometers and old fashioned watches are all analogue devices.
3) Digital signals are coded pulses — they have one of only two values: on or off, true or false, 0 or 1...
4) On/off switches, digital clocks and digital meters are digital devices.

Signals Have to Be Amplified

Both digital and analogue signals weaken as they travel so they need to be amplified along their route. They also pick up random disturbances, called noise.

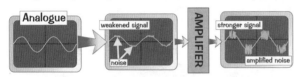

Analogue Signals Lose Quality

Each time it's amplified, the analogue signal gets less and less like the original. The different frequencies in it weaken differently at different times — when the signal is amplified, the differences and noise are amplified too.

Digital Signals Stay The Same

Noise is usually low amplitude so it's just ignored — it's amplified as OFF. Even a weak signal will still be picked up as an ON pulse so it's amplified as ON. The signal stays exactly the same as the original.

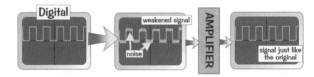

Digital Signals are Far Better Quality

1) Digital signals don't change while they're being transmitted. This makes them higher quality — the information transmitted is the same as the original.
2) Loads more information can be sent as digital signals compared to analogue (in a certain time). Many digital signals can be transmitted at once by a clever way of overlapping them on the same cable or EM wave — but you don't need to learn how they do it, phew.

Analogue can be Converted to Digital and Back Again

Higher

1) Modems convert digital signals into analogue ones and vice versa.
2) Signals from a computer are digital, but phone lines work on analogue signals — so they have to be converted from one form to the other. Modems contain a DAC (digital to analogue converter) — this produces a signal that can travel down a phone line.
3) They also contain an ADC (analogue to digital converter) so the modem at the other end of the line can convert the signal back into digital form.
   You don't have to know how they work, but they're very clever things.

Higher

Pulses are higher quality — especially those nice Heinz ones...

Life would be pretty dull without signals — no phones, no computers, no groovy digital watches.

Diffraction: a Property of all Waves

This word sounds a lot more technical than it really is.

Diffraction is Just the "Spreading Out" of Waves

All waves tend to spread out at the edges when they pass through a gap or past an object. Instead of saying that the wave "spreads out" or "bends" round a corner you should say that it DIFFRACTS around the corner. It's as easy as that. That's all diffraction means.

A Wave Spreads More if it Passes Through a Narrow Gap

The ripple tank shows this effect quite nicely. The same effect applies to light and sound waves too.

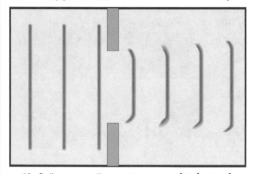
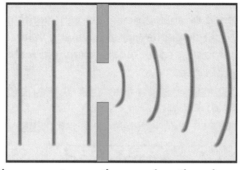
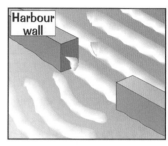

1) A "narrow" gap is one which is about the same size as the wavelength or less.
2) Obviously then, the question of whether a gap is "narrow" or not depends on the wave in question. What may be a narrow gap for a water wave will be a huge gap for a light wave.
3) It should be obvious then, that the longer the wavelength of a wave the more it will diffract.

Sounds Always Diffract Quite a Lot, Because λ is Quite Big

1) Most sounds have wavelengths in air of around 0.1 m, which is quite long.

2) This means they spread out round corners so you can still hear people even when you can't see them directly (the sound usually reflects off walls too which also helps).

3) Higher frequency sounds will have shorter wavelengths and so they won't diffract as much, which is why things sound more "muffled" when you hear them from round corners.

Long Wavelength Radio Waves Diffract Easily Over Hills and into Buildings:

Visible Light on the other hand...

has a very short wavelength, and it'll only diffract with a very narrow slit:

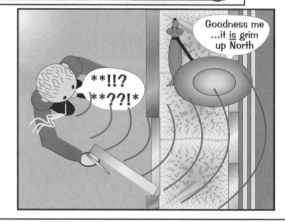

This spreading or diffraction of light (and radio waves) is strong evidence for the wave nature of light.

Diffraction — it can drive you round the bend...

People usually don't know much about diffraction, mainly because there are so few lab demos you can do to show it, and there's also very little to say about it — about one page's worth, in fact. The thing is though, if you just learn this page properly, then you'll know all you need to.

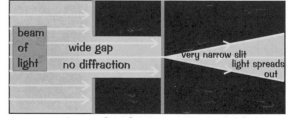

The Electromagnetic Spectrum

The Seven Types of EM Wave Travel At the Same Speed

The properties of electromagnetic waves (EM waves) change as the frequency (or wavelength) changes. We split them into seven basic types as shown below.

These EM waves form a continuous spectrum so the different regions do actually merge into each other.

RADIO WAVES	MICRO WAVES	INFRA RED	VISIBLE LIGHT	ULTRA VIOLET	X-RAYS	GAMMA RAYS
$1m-10^4 m$	$10^{-2} m$ (3cm)	$10^{-5} m$ (0.01mm)	$10^{-7} m$	$10^{-8} m$	$10^{-10} m$	$10^{-12} m$

Our eyes can only detect a very narrow range of EM waves — the ones we call (visible) light.
All EM waves travel at exactly the same speed as light in a vacuum, and pretty much the same speed as light in other media like glass or water — though this is always slower than their speed in vacuum.

As the Wavelength Changes, so do the Properties

1) As the wavelength of EM radiation changes, its interaction with matter changes. In particular, the way any EM wave is absorbed, reflected or transmitted by any given substance depends entirely on its wavelength — that's the whole point of these pages of course.

2) As a rule the EM waves at each end of the spectrum tend to be able to pass through material, whilst those nearer the middle are absorbed.

3) Also, the ones at the top end (high frequency, short wavelength) tend to be the most dangerous, whilst those lower down are generally harmless.

4) When any EM radiation is absorbed it can cause two effects:
   a) Heating   b) Creation of a tiny alternating current with the same frequency as the radiation.

5) You need to know all the details that follow about all the different parts of the EM spectrum:

Radio Waves are Used Mainly for Communications

1) Radio Waves are used mainly for communication and, perhaps more importantly, for controlling model aeroplanes.

2) Both TV and FM Radio use short wavelength radio waves of about 1 m wavelength.

3) To receive these wavelengths you need to be more or less in direct sight of the transmitter, because they will not bend (diffract) over hills or travel very far through buildings.

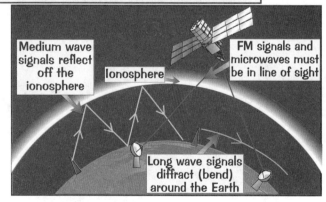

4) Long Wave radio on the other hand has wavelengths of about 1 km and these waves will bend over the surface of the Earth and also diffract into tunnels and all sorts.

5) Medium Wave radio signals which have wavelengths of about 300 m can be received long distances from the transmitter because they are reflected from the ionosphere, which is an electrically charged layer in the Earth's upper atmosphere. Mind you, these signals are always so fuzzy they're not worth listening to anyway (in my humble opinion).

The spectrum — isn't that something kinda rude in Biology...

There are lots of details on this page that you definitely need to know. The top diagram is an absolute must — they usually give it you with one or two missing labels to be filled in. Learn the three sections on this page then scribble a mini-essay for each one to see what you know.

Uses of EM Radiation

Microwaves Are Used For Cooking and Satellite Signals

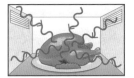

1) <u>Microwaves</u> have <u>two main uses</u>: <u>cooking food</u> and <u>satellite transmissions</u>.

2) The frequency used for satellite transmissions <u>passes easily</u> through the <u>Earth's atmosphere</u>, including <u>clouds</u>, which seems pretty sensible.

3) The frequency used for <u>cooking</u>, on the other hand, is one which is <u>readily absorbed</u> by <u>water molecules</u>. This is how a microwave oven works. The microwaves pass easily <u>into the food</u> and are then <u>absorbed</u> by the <u>water molecules</u> and turn into heat <u>inside the food</u>.

4) Microwaves can therefore be <u>dangerous</u> because they can be absorbed by <u>living tissue</u> and the heat will <u>damage or kill the cells</u>, causing a sort of "<u>cold burn</u>".

Infrared Radiation — Night-Vision and Remote Controls

1) <u>Infrared</u> (or IR) is otherwise known as <u>heat radiation</u>. This is <u>given out</u> by all <u>hot objects</u>. Infrared is readily <u>absorbed</u> by <u>all materials</u> and <u>causes heating</u>.

2) <u>Radiant heaters</u> (i.e. those that <u>glow red</u>, including <u>toasters</u> and <u>grills</u>) use infrared radiation.

3) Infrared is also used for <u>night-vision equipment</u>. This detects <u>heat radiation</u> given off by <u>all objects</u> and turns it into an <u>electrical signal</u> which is <u>displayed on a screen</u> as a clear picture. The <u>hotter</u> an object is, the <u>brighter</u> it appears.

4) Infrared is also used for all TV and video <u>remote controls</u>. It's ideal for sending <u>harmless signals</u> over <u>short distances</u> without <u>interfering</u> with radio frequencies (like the TV channels).

Ultraviolet Light Causes Skin Cancer

1) <u>Skin cancer</u> is caused by spending <u>too much time</u> soaking up the UV rays from the <u>Sun</u>.

2) UV radiation makes you <u>tan</u>. <u>Sunbeds</u> give out fewer UV rays than the Sun but they're still <u>harmful</u>.

3) <u>Tanned or darker skin</u> protects against UV rays — they can't reach more <u>vulnerable tissues</u> below.

4) <u>Special coatings</u> which <u>absorb UV light</u> and then <u>give out visible light</u> instead are used to coat the inside of <u>fluorescent tubes</u> and lamps.

5) UV is also useful for <u>hidden security marks</u> which are written in special ink that can only be seen with an ultraviolet light.

X-Rays are used in Hospitals, but are Pretty Dangerous

1) <u>X-ray photographs</u> are used to see if people have <u>broken bones</u>.

2) X-rays pass <u>easily through flesh</u> but not through <u>denser material</u> like <u>bones</u> or <u>metal</u>.

3) X-rays can cause <u>cancer</u>, so radiographers wear <u>lead aprons</u> and stand behind a <u>lead screen</u> or <u>leave the room</u> to keep their <u>exposure</u> to X-rays to a <u>minimum</u>.

Gamma Rays Treat Cancer Without Surgery

1) Gamma rays kill <u>harmful bacteria</u>, keep food <u>fresher for longer</u> and <u>sterilise medical instruments</u>.

2) In <u>high doses</u>, gamma rays, X-rays and UV rays can <u>kill normal cells</u>. In <u>lower doses</u>, these three types of EM waves can cause normal cells to become <u>cancerous</u>. But if the dose is just right, gamma rays can be used to treat cancer <u>without surgery</u> because they <u>kill cancer cells</u>.

I want a remote control / grill combo — to cook pizzas from my armchair...

And visible light is also pretty useful. We use it for <u>seeing</u> with for one thing. It's also used in <u>Optical Fibre Digital Communications</u> (which is the best use by far for your answer <u>in the Exam</u>).

The Planets

You need to revise the <u>order</u> of the planets, which is made easier by using the little jollyism below:

Mercury,	Venus,	Earth,	Mars,	(Asteroids),	Jupiter,	Saturn,	Uranus,	Neptune,	Pluto
(My	Very	Energetic	Maiden	Aunt	Just	Swam	Under	North	Pier)

<u>Mercury</u>, <u>Venus</u>, <u>Earth</u> and <u>Mars</u> are known as the <u>inner planets</u>.

<u>Jupiter</u>, <u>Saturn</u>, <u>Uranus</u>, <u>Neptune</u> and <u>Pluto</u> are much further away and are the <u>outer planets</u>.

Planets Reflect Sunlight and Orbit in Ellipses

1) You can <u>see</u> some of the nearer planets with the <u>naked eye</u> at night, e.g. Mars and Venus.
2) They look just like <u>stars</u>, but they are of course <u>totally different</u>.
3) Stars are <u>huge</u> and <u>very far away</u> and <u>give out</u> lots of light.
   The planets are <u>smaller</u> and <u>nearer</u> and they just <u>reflect sunlight</u> falling on them.
4) The Sun, like other stars, produces <u>heat</u> from <u>nuclear fusion reactions</u> which turn <u>hydrogen</u> into <u>helium</u>. It gives out the <u>full spectrum</u> of <u>EM radiation</u>.
5) Planets orbit around <u>stars</u>. In our Solar System the planets orbit the <u>Sun</u> of course.
6) These orbits are all <u>slightly elliptical</u> (elongated circles).
7) All the planets in our Solar System orbit in the <u>same plane</u> except Pluto (as shown in the pic above).
8) The <u>further</u> the planet is from the Sun, the <u>longer</u> its orbit takes (see below about gravity).

Gravity Decreases Quickly as you get Further Away

1) With <u>very large</u> masses like <u>stars</u> and <u>planets</u>, gravity is <u>very big</u> and acts <u>a long way out</u>.
2) The <u>closer</u> you get to a star or a planet, the <u>stronger</u> the <u>force of attraction</u>.
3) To <u>counteract</u> the stronger gravity, planets nearer the Sun move <u>faster</u> and cover their orbit <u>quicker</u>.
4) <u>Comets</u> are also held in <u>orbit</u> by gravity, as are <u>moons</u> and <u>satellites</u> and <u>space stations</u>.
5) The size of the force of gravity follows the fairly famous "<u>inverse square</u>" relationship.
   The main effect of that is that the force <u>decreases very quickly</u> with increasing <u>distance</u>.
   The <u>formula</u> is $F \propto 1/d^2$, but I reckon it's <u>easier</u> just to remember the basic idea <u>in words</u>:

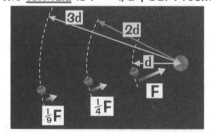

a) If you <u>double the distance</u> from a planet, the size of the <u>force</u> will <u>decrease</u> by a <u>factor of four</u> (2^2).

b) If you <u>treble the distance</u>, the <u>force</u> of gravity will <u>decrease</u> by a <u>factor of nine</u> (3^2), and so on.

c) On the other hand, if you get <u>twice as close</u> the gravity becomes <u>four times stronger</u>.

Planets in the Night Sky Seem to Move across the Constellations

1) The <u>planets</u> look just like stars except that they <u>wander</u> across the constellations over periods of <u>days or weeks</u>, often going in the <u>opposite direction</u> to the stars.
2) Their position and movement depends on <u>where</u> they are in their orbit, compared to <u>us</u>.
3) This <u>peculiar movement</u> of the planets made the <u>early astronomers</u> realise that the Earth was <u>not the centre</u> of the Universe after all, but was in fact just the <u>third rock from the Sun</u>. It's <u>very strong evidence</u> for the <u>Sun-centred</u> model of the Solar System.

If you're gonna revise properly you'd better planet first...

Isn't the Solar System great. All those pretty coloured planets and all that big black empty space. You can look forward to one or two easy questions on the planets — or you might get two real horrors instead. Be ready — <u>learn</u> all the <u>details</u> till you know it all real good.

Satellites and Comets

Moons are sometimes called <u>natural satellites</u>. But there are <u>man-made</u> satellites too.

Moons Orbit Planets

1) The Earth only has <u>one</u> moon of course, but some of the <u>other planets</u> have <u>quite a few</u>.

2) We can only <u>see</u> the moon because it <u>reflects sunlight</u>.

3) The <u>phases of the moon</u> happen depending on <u>how much</u> of the <u>illuminated side</u> of the moon we can <u>see</u>, as shown.

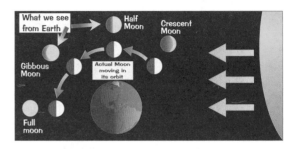

Geostationary Satellites are Used For Communications

1) These can also be called *geosynchronous* satellites.

2) They are put in <u>quite a high orbit</u> over the <u>Equator</u> which takes <u>exactly 24 hours</u> to complete.

3) This means that they <u>stay above the same point</u> on the Earth's surface because the Earth <u>rotates with them</u> — hence the name Geo(*Earth*)-stationary.

4) This makes them <u>ideal</u> for <u>telephone</u> and <u>TV</u> because they're always in the <u>same place</u> and they can <u>transfer signals</u> from one side of the Earth to another in a <u>fraction of a second</u>.

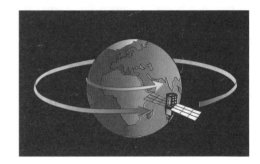

Low Polar Orbit Satellites are for Weather and Spying

1) In a <u>low polar orbit</u>, the satellite sweeps over <u>both poles</u> whilst the Earth <u>rotates beneath it</u>.

2) The time taken for each full orbit is just <u>a few hours</u>.

3) Each time the satellite comes round it can <u>scan</u> the next bit of the globe.

4) This allows the <u>whole surface</u> of the planet to be <u>monitored</u> each day.

5) Geostationary satellites are <u>too high</u> to take good weather or spying photos, but the satellites in <u>polar orbits</u> are <u>nice and low</u>.

Comets Orbit the Sun, but have very Eccentric (elongated) Orbits

1) <u>Comets</u> only appear <u>every few years</u> because their <u>orbits</u> take them <u>very far from the Sun</u> and then <u>back in close</u>, which is when <u>we</u> see them.

2) The Sun is <u>not at the centre</u> of the orbit but <u>near one end</u> as shown.

3) Comet <u>orbits</u> can be in <u>different planes</u> from the orbits of the planets.

4) The comet travels <u>much faster</u> when it's <u>nearer the Sun</u> than when it's in the more <u>distant</u> part of its orbit. This is because the <u>pull of gravity</u> makes it <u>speed up</u> as it gets <u>closer</u>, and then <u>slows it down</u> as it gets <u>further away</u> from the Sun.

Learn about Satellites — and look down on your friends...

You can actually see the low polar orbit satellites on a nice dark clear night. They look like stars except they move quite fast in a dead straight line across the sky. You're never gonna spot the geostationary ones though. <u>Learn all the details</u> about satellites, ready for seizing juicy marks.

Searching for Life on Other Planets

There's a good chance that life exists somewhere else in the Universe.
Scientists use <u>three methods</u> to search for anything from amoebas to little green men.

1) SETI Looks for Radio Signals from Other Planets

Higher

1) Us Earthlings are constantly beaming <u>radio</u>, <u>TV</u> and <u>radar</u> into space for any passing aliens to detect. There might be life out there that's as clever as we are. Or even more clever. They may have built <u>transmitters</u> to send out signals like ours.

2) <u>SETI</u> stands for "Search for Extra Terrestrial Intelligence". Scientists on the SETI project are looking for <u>narrow bands</u> of <u>radio wavelengths</u> coming to Earth from outer space. They're looking for <u>meaningful signals</u> in all the '<u>noise</u>' (see P.93)

3) Signals on a narrow band can <u>only</u> come from a <u>transmitter</u>. The 'noise' comes from giant stars and gas clouds.

4) It takes <u>ages</u> to analyse all the radio waves so the SETI folk get help from the public — you can download a <u>screen saver</u> off the internet which analyses a chunk of radio waves.
5) SETI has been going for the last <u>40 years</u> but they've <u>not found anything</u>. Not a sausage. ☹
6) Scientists are now looking for possible <u>laser</u> signals from outer space. Watch this space...

2) Robots Collect Photos and Samples

This <u>could</u> be a microscopic fossil of a bacteria-like organism from Mars.

Then again, it could be a crystal, bits of metal or the remains of last night's curry... 500 nm

1) Scientists have sent robots in spacecrafts to <u>Mars</u> and <u>Europa</u> (one of Jupiter's moons) to look for microorganisms.
2) The robots wander round the planet, sending <u>photographs</u> back to Earth or <u>collecting samples</u> for analysis.
3) Scientists can detect living things or <u>evidence</u> of them, such as <u>fossils</u> or <u>remains</u>, in the samples. This "fossil" is from Mars, though no one really seems sure *what* it is.
4) OK, so a couple of bacteria is a bit boring but that's how we started out on Earth...

3) Chemical Changes and Reflected Light Are Big Clues

Changes Show There's Life

1) Scientists are looking for <u>chemical changes</u> in the atmospheres of other planets.
2) They look at planets' atmospheres from Earth — no spacecraft required.
3) Some changes are just caused by things like volcanoes, but others are a <u>clue</u> that there's life there.
4) The amounts of <u>oxygen</u> and <u>carbon dioxide</u> in Earth's atmosphere have <u>changed</u> over time — it's <u>very different</u> to what it'd be like if there was <u>no life</u> here. Plants have made oxygen levels <u>go up</u> but carbon dioxide levels <u>go down</u>.

Light Gives Away What's On The Surface

A planet's <u>reflected light</u> (from the Sun) is <u>different</u> depending on whether it's bounced off rock, trees, water or whatever. It's a good way to find out what's on the <u>surface</u> of a planet.

Scientists haven't found anything exciting (surprise surprise) but they are using these methods to search for planets with <u>suitable conditions</u> for life.

I've got SETI — it's great for watching telly on...

You need to learn these <u>three</u> different ways that scientists are looking for life on other planets. You definitely need to learn this stuff, even if you get given more information in the exam. Cover the page and write notes about <u>how</u> the methods work and <u>what</u> they've found.

The Universe

Stars and Solar Systems form from Clouds of Dust

1) Stars form from <u>clouds of dust</u> which <u>spiral in together</u> due to <u>gravitational attraction</u>.

2) The gravity <u>compresses</u> the matter so much that <u>intense heat</u> develops and sets off <u>nuclear fusion reactions</u> and the star then begins <u>emitting light</u> and other <u>radiation</u>.

3) At the <u>same time</u> that the star is forming, <u>other lumps</u> may develop in the <u>spiralling dust clouds</u> and these eventually gather together and form <u>planets</u> which orbit <u>around the star</u>.

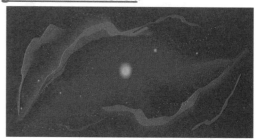

Our Sun is in The Milky Way Galaxy

1) The <u>Sun</u> is one of <u>many millions</u> of <u>stars</u> which form the <u>Milky Way Galaxy</u>.

2) The <u>distance</u> between neighbouring stars is usually <u>millions of times greater</u> than the distance between <u>planets</u> in our Solar System.

3) <u>Gravity</u> is of course the <u>force</u> which keeps the stars <u>together</u> in a <u>galaxy</u> and, like most things in the Universe, the <u>galaxies all rotate</u>, kinda like a Catherine wheel only <u>much slower</u>.

You are here

4) Our Sun is out towards the <u>end</u> of one of the <u>spiral arms</u> of the Milky Way galaxy.

You are here

The Whole Universe has More Than A Billion Galaxies

1) <u>Galaxies</u> themselves are often <u>millions of times further apart</u> than the <u>stars</u> are within a galaxy.

2) So even the slowest amongst you will soon begin to realise that the Universe is <u>mostly empty space</u> and is <u>really really big</u>. Have you ever been to the NEC? Yeah? Well, it's even bigger than that.

Black Holes Don't Let Anything Escape

1) The gravity on neutron stars, white dwarfs and black dwarfs (see next page) is <u>so strong</u> that it <u>crushes atoms</u>. The stuff in the stars gets <u>squashed up</u> so much that they're <u>MILLIONS OF TIMES DENSER</u> than anything on Earth.

2) If <u>enough</u> matter is left behind after a supernova explosion, it's <u>so dense</u> that <u>nothing</u> can escape the powerful gravitional field. Not even electromagnetic waves. The dead star is then called a <u>black hole</u>. Black holes <u>aren't visible</u> because any light being emitted is sucked right back in there (that's why it's called 'black', d'oh).

3) Astronomers can detect black holes in other ways — e.g. they can observe <u>X-rays</u> emitted by <u>hot gases</u> from other stars as they spiral into the black hole.

Galaxies, Milky Way — shove that down yer black hole...

More gripping facts about the Universe. Just look at those numbers: there's <u>billions</u> of stars in the Milky Way, the universe contains <u>billions</u> of galaxies, all <u>many times</u> further apart than 100 000 light years... Doesn't it just blow your socks off...

The Life Cycle of Stars

Stars go through <u>many traumatic stages</u> in their lives — just like teenagers.

Clouds of Dust and Gas

1) Stars <u>initially form</u> from clouds of *DUST AND GAS*.

Protostar

2) The <u>force of gravity</u> makes the dust particles come <u>spiralling in together</u>. As they do, <u>gravitational energy</u> is converted into <u>heat energy</u> and the <u>temperature rises</u>.

Main Sequence Star

3) When the <u>temperature</u> gets <u>high enough</u>, <u>hydrogen nuclei</u> undergo <u>nuclear fusion</u> to form <u>helium nuclei</u> and give out massive amounts of <u>heat and light</u>. A star is born. It immediately enters a <u>long stable period</u> where the <u>heat created</u> by the nuclear fusion provides an <u>outward pressure</u> to <u>balance</u> the <u>force of gravity</u> pulling everything <u>inwards</u>. In this stable period it's called a *MAIN SEQUENCE STAR* and it typically lasts about <u>10 billion years</u>. (The Sun is in the middle of this stable period — or to put it another way, the <u>Earth</u> has already had <u>half its innings</u> before the Sun <u>engulfs</u> it.)

4) Eventually the <u>hydrogen</u> begins to <u>run out</u> and the star then <u>swells</u> into a *RED GIANT*. It becomes <u>red</u> because the surface <u>cools</u>.

5) A <u>small star</u> like our Sun will then begin to <u>cool</u> and <u>contract</u> into a *WHITE DWARF* and then finally, as the <u>light fades completely</u>, it becomes a *BLACK DWARF*. (That's going to be really sad.)

Red Giant

Small stars

White Dwarf

Black Dwarf

Big stars

6) <u>Big stars</u> however, start to <u>glow brightly again</u> as they undergo more <u>fusion</u> and <u>expand and contract several times</u> forming <u>heavier elements</u> in various <u>nuclear reactions</u>. Eventually they'll <u>explode</u> in a *SUPERNOVA*.

new planetary nebula...

...and a new solar system

Supernova

Neutron Star...

...or Black Hole

7) The <u>exploding supernova</u> throws the outer layers of <u>dust and gas</u> into space leaving a <u>very dense core</u> called a *NEUTRON STAR*. If the star is <u>big enough</u> this will become a *BLACK HOLE*.

8) The <u>dust and gas</u> thrown off by the supernova will form into *SECOND GENERATION STARS* like our Sun. The <u>heavier elements</u> are <u>only</u> made in the <u>final stages</u> of a <u>big star</u> just before and during the final <u>supernova</u>, so the <u>presence</u> of heavier elements in the <u>Sun</u> and the <u>inner planets</u> is <u>clear evidence</u> that our beautiful and wonderful world, with its warm sunsets and fresh morning dews, has all formed out of the snotty remains of a grisly old star's last dying sneeze.

9) The <u>matter</u> from which <u>neutron stars</u> and <u>white dwarfs</u> and <u>black dwarfs</u> are made is <u>MILLIONS OF TIMES DENSER</u> than any matter on Earth because the <u>gravity is so strong</u> it even crushes the <u>atoms</u>.

Twinkle Twinkle little star, How I wond.. — JUST LEARN IT PAL...

Erm. Just how do they know all that? As if it's not outrageous enough that they reckon to know the whole history of the Earth for the last 4.6 billion years, they also reckon to know the whole life cycle of stars, when they're all billions and billions of km away. It's just an outrage.

The Origin of the Universe

The <u>Big Bang Theory</u> of the Universe is the <u>most convincing</u> at the present time. There is also the <u>steady state theory</u>, which is quite presentable but it <u>doesn't explain</u> some of the observed features too well.

Red-shift and Background Radiation need Explaining

There are <u>three important bits of evidence</u> you need to know about:

1) Light From Other Galaxies is Red-Shifted

1) When we look at <u>light from distant galaxies</u> we find that <u>all the frequencies</u> are <u>shifted</u> towards the <u>red end</u> of the spectrum.

2) In other words, the <u>frequencies</u> are all <u>slightly lower</u> than they should be. It's the same effect as a car <u>horn</u> sounding lower-pitched when the car is travelling <u>away</u> from you. The sound <u>drops in frequency</u>.

3) This is called the *DOPPLER EFFECT*.

4) <u>Measurements</u> of the red-shift suggest that <u>all the galaxies</u> are <u>moving away from us</u> very quickly — and it's the <u>same result</u> whichever direction you look in.

2) The Further Away a Galaxy is, The Greater The Red-Shift

1) <u>More distant</u> galaxies have <u>greater</u> red-shifts than nearer ones.

2) This means that more distant galaxies are <u>moving away faster</u> than nearer ones.

3) The inescapable <u>conclusion</u> appears to be that the whole Universe is <u>expanding</u>.

3) There's a Uniform Microwave Radiation From All Directions

1) This <u>low frequency radiation</u> comes from <u>all directions</u> and from <u>all parts</u> of the Universe.

2) It's known as the <u>background radiation</u> (of the Big Bang). It's nothing to do with radioactive background radiation on Earth.

3) For complicated reasons this background radiation is <u>strong evidence</u> for an <u>initial Big Bang</u>, and as the Universe <u>expands and cools</u>, so this background radiation "<u>cools</u>" and <u>drops in frequency</u>.

The Steady State Theory of the Universe — Not Popular

1) This is based on the idea that the Universe appears pretty much the <u>same everywhere</u> and <u>always has done</u>.

2) In other words the Universe has <u>always existed</u> and <u>always will</u> in the same form that it is now.

3) This theory explains the <u>apparent expansion</u> of the Universe by suggesting that <u>matter</u> is being <u>created</u> in the spaces as the Universe expands.

4) However, as yet, there's <u>no convincing explanation</u> of <u>where</u> this new matter <u>comes from</u>.

5) There isn't much support for the steady state theory, especially since the discovery of <u>background radiation</u>, which fits in <u>much better</u> with the idea of a Big Bang.

6) But you <u>just never know</u>...

The Origin and Future of the Universe

The Big Bang Theory — Well Popular

1) Since all the galaxies appear to be <u>moving apart</u> very rapidly, the <u>obvious conclusion</u> is that there was an <u>initial explosion</u>: the <u>Big Bang</u>.

2) All the matter in the Universe must have been <u>compressed into a very small space</u> and then it <u>exploded</u> and the <u>expansion</u> is still going on.

3) The Big Bang is believed to have happened around <u>15 billion years ago</u>.

4) The age of the Universe can be <u>estimated</u> from the <u>current rate of expansion</u>.

5) These estimates are <u>not very accurate</u> because it's hard to tell how much the expansion has <u>slowed down</u> since the Big Bang.

6) The rate at which the expansion is <u>slowing down</u> is an <u>important factor</u> in deciding the <u>future</u> of the Universe.

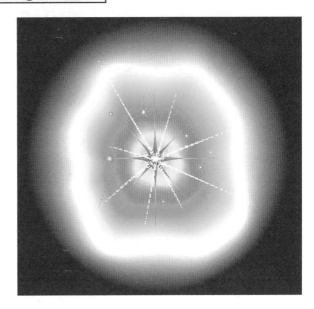

7) <u>Without gravity</u> the Universe would expand at the <u>same rate forever</u>.

8) However, the <u>attraction</u> between all the mass in the Universe tends to <u>slow</u> the expansion down.

The Future of the Universe:

It Could Expand Forever — or Collapse into The Big Crunch

1) The eventual fate of the Universe depends on <u>how fast</u> the galaxies are <u>moving apart</u> and how much <u>total mass</u> there is in it.

2) We can <u>measure</u> how fast the galaxies are <u>separating</u> quite easily, but we'd also like to know just <u>how much mass</u> there is in the Universe in order to <u>predict the future</u> of it.

3) This is proving <u>tricky</u> as most of the mass appears to be <u>invisible</u>, e.g. <u>black holes</u>, <u>big planets</u>, <u>interstellar dust</u> etc.

Anyway, depending on <u>how much mass</u> there is, there are <u>two ways</u> the Universe could go:

1) Le Crunch — But Only if there's Enough Mass

If there's <u>enough mass</u> compared to <u>how fast</u> the galaxies are currently moving, the Universe will eventually <u>stop expanding</u> and <u>begin contracting</u>. This would end in a <u>Big Crunch</u>. The Big Crunch could be followed by another Big Bang and then <u>endless cycles</u> of <u>expansion and contraction</u>.

2) If there's Too Little Mass — then it's Le Miserable Eternity

If there's <u>too little mass</u> in the Universe to slow the expansion down, then it could <u>expand forever</u> with the Universe becoming <u>more and more spread out</u> into eternity. This seems <u>way too dismal</u> for my liking. I much prefer the idea of the Universe going <u>endlessly in cycles</u>.
But what was there <u>before</u> the Universe? Or what is there <u>outside</u> of it? It's <u>mindboggling</u>.

Time and Space — it's funny old stuff isn't it...

I think it's great that they've put all this stuff on space in the syllabus. I mean wow, something in Physics that's actually interesting. The great thing about learning a few bits and bobs about the Universe is that it can make you sound really clever when you tell people about it. "Ah well, it's all to do with the diminishing Doppler red-shift over the last 15 billion years," you can say.

Revision Summary for Section Eight

The Universe is completely mindblowing. But surely the most mindblowing thing of all is the very fact that we are actually here, sitting and contemplating the truly outrageous improbability of our own existence. If your mind isn't blowing, then it hasn't sunk in yet. Think about it. 15 billion years ago there was a huge explosion, but there was no need for the whole chain of events to happen which allowed (or caused?) intelligent life to evolve and develop to the point where it became conscious of its own existence, not to mention the very disturbing unlikelihood of it all. But we have. We're here. Maaaan — is that freaky or what? The Universe could so easily have existed without conscious life ever evolving. Or come to that, the Universe needn't exist at all. Just black nothingness. So why does it exist? And why are we here? And why do we have to do so much revision? Who knows — but stop dreaming and get on with it.

1) Define the frequency and time period for a wave.
2) Sketch transverse and longtitudinal waves. Define them and give examples of both types.
3) What's the connection between amplitude and the energy carried by a wave?
4) What effect does greater amplitude have on a) sound waves b) light waves?
5) What's the relationship between frequency and pitch for a sound wave?
6) Sketch CRO screens showing higher and lower pitch and quiet and loud sounds.
7) What is ultrasound? Give full details of three applications of ultrasound.
8) Sketch the patterns when plane ripples reflect at a) a plane surface, b) a curved surface.
9) Sketch the reflection of curved ripples at a plane surface.
10) What is the law of reflection? Give a sketch to illustrate diffuse reflection of light.
11) Draw a neat ray diagram to show how to locate the position of the image in a plane mirror.
12) What is refraction? What causes it? How does it affect wavelength and frequency?
13) Sketch a ray of light going through a rectangular glass block, showing the angles i and r.
14) Sketch three diagrams to illustrate Total Internal Reflection and the Critical Angle.
15) Give details of the two main uses of optical fibres. How do optical fibres work?
16) Describe analogue and digital signals. What are the advantages of digital signals?
17) What is diffraction? Sketch the diffraction of a) water waves b) sound waves c) light.
18) What aspect of EM waves determines their differing properties?
19) Sketch the EM spectrum with all its details. What happens when EM waves are absorbed?
20) Give full details of two uses of microwaves, and three uses of infrared.
21) Detail three uses of UV light, two uses of X-rays and three uses of gamma rays.
22) What harm will UV, X-rays and gamma rays do in <u>high</u> doses? What about in <u>low</u> doses?
23) List the ten parts of the Solar System starting with the Sun, and get them in the right order.
24) How does the Sun produce all its heat? What does the Sun give out?
25) Which planet has an unusual orbit?
26) What is it that keeps the planets in their orbits? What shape are their orbits?
27) What is the famous "inverse square" relationship all about? Sketch a diagram to explain it.
28) Sketch a diagram to explain the phases of the moon.
29) What are natural and artificial satellites?
30) Explain fully what a geostationary satellite does, and state what they're used for.
31) Explain fully what a low polar orbit satellite does, and state what they're used for.
32) What and where are comets? What are they made of? Sketch a diagram of a comet orbit.
33) What does SETI stand for? Why are they looking for narrow band signals?
34) Describe two ways that scientists look for life on planets without sending spacecraft there.
35) What do stars and solar systems form from? What force causes it all to happen?
36) What is the Universe made up of? How big is it?
37) What's odd about the gravity on neutron stars, white dwarfs and black dwarfs?
38) Why would a black hole form? Why's it called 'black'? How can you spot one?
39) Describe the first stages of a star's formation. Where does the initial energy come from?
40) What process eventually starts inside the star to make it produce so much heat and light?
41) What is meant by a "second generation" star? How do we know our Sun is one?
42) What are the two main theories of the origin of the universe? Which one is more likely to be true?
43) What are the three important bits of evidence which need explaining by these theories?
44) Give brief details of both theories. How long ago did each suggest the Universe began?

Speed, Velocity and Acceleration

Speed, Velocity and Acceleration

1) Speed and velocity are both measured in m/s (or km/h or mph), but there's a subtle difference:

> Speed is just how fast you're going (e.g. 40 m/s) with no regard to the direction.
>
> Velocity however must also have the direction specified, e.g. 40 m/s, 060°.

The *Speed / Velocity* Formula

$$\text{Speed} = \frac{\text{Distance}}{\text{Time}}$$

The *Acceleration* Formula

$$\text{Acceleration} = \frac{\text{Change in Velocity}}{\text{Time Taken}}$$

2) Acceleration is definitely not the same as velocity or speed. Acceleration involves a change in either speed or direction.

3) So acceleration is the 'velocity change per unit time'.

4) The units of acceleration are m/s^2. Not m/s, which is velocity, but m/s^2.

EXAMPLE 1: A cat skulks 20 m in 35 s. Find its speed.
ANSWER: Using the formula triangle: a) $s = d/t = 20/35 = $ __0.57 m/s__

EXAMPLE 2: A skulking cat accelerates from 2 m/s to 6 m/s in 5.6 s. Find its acceleration.
ANSWER: Using the formula triangle: $a = \Delta V/t = (6 - 2) / 5.6 = 4 \div 5.6 = $ __0.71 m/s²__

Distance-Time Graphs

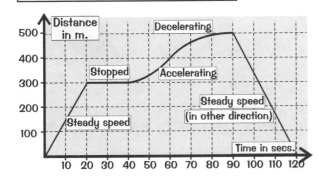

Very Important Notes:

1) GRADIENT = SPEED.
2) Flat sections are where it's stopped.
3) The steeper the graph, the faster it's going.
4) Downhill sections mean it's coming back toward its starting point.
5) Curves represent acceleration or deceleration.
6) A steepening curve means it's speeding up (increasing gradient).
7) A levelling off curve means it's slowing down (decreasing gradient).

Calculating Speed from a Distance-Time Graph — it's just the Gradient

For example the speed of the return section of the graph is:

$\text{Speed} = \text{gradient} = \dfrac{\text{vertical}}{\text{horizontal}} = \dfrac{500}{30} = $ __16.7 m/s__

Don't forget that you have to use the scales of the axes to work out the gradient. Don't measure in cm.

Velocity-Time Graphs

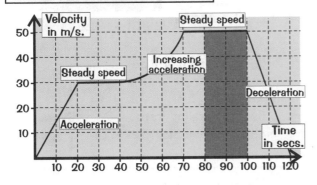

Very Important Notes:

1) GRADIENT = ACCELERATION.
2) Flat sections represent steady speed.
3) The steeper the graph, the greater the acceleration or deceleration.
4) Uphill sections (/) are acceleration.
5) Downhill sections (\) — deceleration.
6) The area under any section of the graph (or all of it) is equal to the distance travelled in that time interval.
7) A curve means changing acceleration.

Come on — it's not rocket science...

Make sure you know all about this speed and acceleration malarky because there are loads of different questions they can ask in the Exam. Cover up the page, and write down what you remember.

Forces and Motion

Make sure you learn all these details real good.

Newton's Three Laws of Motion

forces balance, so steady speed

1) **Newton's First Law:** If the <u>forces</u> on an object are all <u>balanced</u> then:
   (i) If it's <u>stationary</u>, it'll just <u>stay still</u>.
   (ii) If it's <u>already moving</u>, it'll keep moving with the <u>same velocity</u>.

2) **Newton's Second Law:** An <u>unbalanced force</u> always produces an <u>acceleration</u> (or deceleration).

unbalanced forces, so accelerating

3) This 'acceleration' results in the object <u>starting to move</u>, <u>stopping</u>, <u>speeding up</u>, <u>slowing down</u> or <u>changing direction</u>.

4) The <u>formula</u> relating <u>force (F)</u>, <u>mass (m)</u> and <u>acceleration (a)</u> is:

$$F = ma \quad \text{or} \quad a = F/m$$

5) **Newton's Third Law:** If an object A <u>exerts a force</u> on an object B, then object B exerts <u>the exact opposite force</u> on object A.

6) This means, for example, that if you <u>push against a wall</u>, the wall will <u>push back</u> against you, <u>just as hard</u>. And as soon as you <u>stop</u> pushing, <u>so does the wall</u>.

Calculations using F = ma — an Example

<u>Question:</u> What force is needed to accelerate a mass of 12 kg at 5 m/s² ?

<u>Answer</u>: The question is asking for <u>force</u> — so you need a formula with "<u>F = something-or-other</u>".

Since they also give you values for <u>mass</u> and <u>acceleration</u>, the formula "<u>F = ma</u>" really should be a <u>pretty obvious choice</u>, surely.

So just <u>stick in the numbers</u> they give you where the letters are:
<u>m = 12</u>, <u>a = 5</u>, so "<u>F = ma</u>" gives F = 12 × 5 = <u>60 N</u>   (It's <u>Newtons</u> because force always is.)
(Notice that you don't need to <u>fully understand</u> what's going on — you just need to know <u>how to use formulas</u>.)

Gravity is the Force of Attraction Between All Masses

1) <u>Gravity</u> attracts <u>all masses</u>, but you only notice it when one of the masses is <u>really big</u>, e.g. the Earth.

2) On Earth, gravity makes all things <u>accelerate</u> towards the <u>centre of the planet</u> with the <u>same acceleration</u>, g, equal to <u>10 m/s²</u>. (g is <u>constant</u> and sometimes called the <u>acceleration of free fall</u>.)

3) <u>Weight</u> is not the same as mass. Weight is a <u>force</u> and is measured in <u>Newtons</u>. Mass is <u>not</u> a force and is measured in <u>kilograms</u>.

4) Weight is caused by the <u>pull of gravity</u> on a mass. A 1 kg mass has the <u>same mass</u> whether it's on Earth or on the Moon, but it will <u>weigh less</u> on the Moon than it does on Earth because the force of gravity pulling on it is <u>smaller</u>.

$$W = m \times g$$
(Weight = mass × g)

5) There is a very <u>important formula</u> relating <u>weight</u>, <u>mass</u> and <u>gravity:</u>

Objects in Free-Fall Reach a Terminal Velocity

1) When a free-falling object <u>first sets off</u> it has <u>much more</u> force <u>accelerating</u> it than <u>air resistance</u> slowing it down.

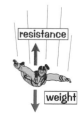
resistance
weight

2) As its <u>speed</u> increases the resistance <u>builds up</u>. This gradually <u>reduces</u> the <u>acceleration</u> until eventually the <u>resistance force</u> is <u>equal</u> to the <u>accelerating force</u>.

3) When the forces balance, it doesn't accelerate any more and has reached its <u>terminal velocity</u>.

Learning about air resistance can be a real drag...

It looks like mini-essay time to me. There's a whole host of details swirling around here, so definitely the best way of checking how much you know is to <u>scribble down a mini-essay</u> for each of the sections. Then <u>check back</u> and see what you <u>missed</u>. Then try again.

Energy Transfer & Energy Conservation

Learn all the Ten Types of Energy

You should know all of these <u>well enough</u> by now to list them <u>from memory</u>, including the examples:

1) <u>ELECTRICAL</u> ENERGY....................................... — whenever a <u>current</u> flows.
2) <u>LIGHT</u> ENERGY... — from the <u>Sun</u>, <u>light bulbs</u> etc.
3) <u>SOUND</u> ENERGY... — from <u>loudspeakers</u> or anything <u>noisy</u>.
4) <u>KINETIC</u> ENERGY, or <u>MOVEMENT</u> ENERGY........ — anything that's <u>moving</u> has it.
5) <u>NUCLEAR</u> ENERGY....................................... — released only from <u>nuclear reactions</u>.
6) <u>THERMAL</u> ENERGY or <u>HEAT</u> ENERGY............... — <u>flows</u> from <u>hot objects</u> to colder ones.
7) <u>RADIANT HEAT</u> ENERGY, or <u>INFRARED</u> HEAT..... — given out as <u>EM radiation</u> by <u>hot objects</u>.
8) <u>GRAVITATIONAL POTENTIAL</u> ENERGY............... — possessed by anything which can <u>fall</u>.
9) <u>ELASTIC POTENTIAL</u> ENERGY...................... — stretched <u>springs</u>, <u>elastic</u>, <u>rubber bands</u>, etc.
10) <u>CHEMICAL</u> ENERGY.................................. — possessed by <u>foods</u>, <u>fuels</u> and <u>batteries</u>.

Potential- and Chemical- are forms of Stored Energy

The <u>last three</u> above are forms of <u>stored energy</u> because the energy is not obviously <u>doing</u> anything, it's kind of <u>waiting to happen</u>, i.e. waiting to be turned into one of the <u>other</u> forms.

They Like Giving Exam Questions on Energy Transfers

These are <u>very important examples</u>. You must <u>learn them</u> till you can repeat them all <u>easily</u>.

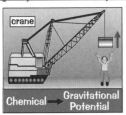 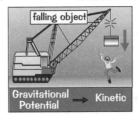 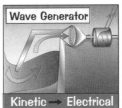 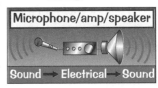
 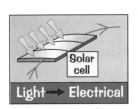  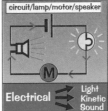 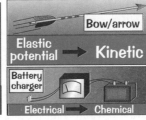 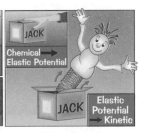

Energy Conservation — You can't Create or Destroy Energy...

The "<u>PRINCIPLE OF THE CONSERVATION OF ENERGY</u>" is one of the <u>major cornerstones</u> of modern Physics. It's an <u>all-pervading principle</u> which governs the workings of the <u>entire physical Universe</u>. If this principle were not so, then life as we know it would simply cease to be.

> <u>**ENERGY**</u> can never be <u>**CREATED**</u> nor <u>**DESTROYED**</u>
> — it's only ever <u>**CONVERTED**</u> from one form to another.

Another <u>important principle</u> which you need to <u>learn</u> is this one:

> Energy is <u>**ONLY USEFUL**</u> when it's <u>**CONVERTED**</u> from one form to another.

Learn about Energy — and just keep working at it...

<u>Energy conservation</u> can also mean <u>using less fossil fuels</u> because of the damage they do to the environment and because they might <u>run out</u>. But that's all very different to the energy conservation mentioned above. Cover the page and write the stuff down 'til you get it all right.

Efficiency

Energy gets converted from one form to another — but some usually gets 'lost' in the process.

Most Energy Transfers Involve Some Losses, as Heat

1) <u>Useful devices</u> are only <u>useful</u> because they <u>convert</u> <u>energy</u> from <u>one form</u> to <u>another</u>.
2) In doing so, some of the useful <u>input energy</u> is always <u>lost or wasted</u>, often as <u>heat</u>.
3) The <u>less energy</u> that is <u>wasted</u>, the <u>more efficient</u> the device is said to be.
4) The <u>energy flow diagram</u> is pretty much the same for <u>all</u> <u>devices</u>. You <u>must</u> learn this <u>basic energy flow diagram</u>:

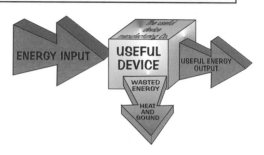

Efficiency measures How Much Energy gets Wasted

A <u>machine</u> is a device which turns <u>one type of energy</u> into <u>another</u>.
The <u>efficiency</u> of any device is defined as:

$$\text{Efficiency} = \frac{\textit{USEFUL Energy OUTPUT}}{\textit{TOTAL Energy INPUT}}$$

$$\frac{\text{Energy out}}{\text{Efficiency} \times \text{Energy in}}$$

You can give efficiency as a <u>fraction</u>, <u>decimal</u> or <u>percentage</u>, e.g. ¾ or 0.75 or 75%

1) You find how much energy is <u>supplied</u> to a machine. (The Total Energy <u>INPUT</u>.)
2) You find how much <u>useful energy</u> the machine <u>delivers</u>. (The Useful Energy <u>OUTPUT</u>.)
   They either tell you this directly or they tell you how much it <u>wastes</u> as heat/sound.
3) Either way, you get those <u>two important numbers</u> and then just <u>divide</u> the <u>smaller one</u> by the <u>bigger one</u> to get a value for <u>efficiency</u> somewhere between <u>0 and 1</u> (or <u>0 and 100%</u>). Easy.
4) The other way they might ask it is to tell you the <u>efficiency</u> and the <u>input energy</u> and ask for the <u>energy output</u>. The best way to tackle that is to <u>learn</u> this <u>other version</u> of the formula:

$$\underline{\textit{USEFUL ENERGY OUTPUT}} = \text{Efficiency} \times \textit{TOTAL Energy INPUT}$$

You can often give <u>more detail</u> about the <u>types</u> of energy being <u>input</u> and <u>output</u>, but <u>remember</u>:

<u>NO</u> device is 100% efficient and the <u>WASTED ENERGY</u> is always <u>dissipated</u> as <u>HEAT</u> and <u>SOUND</u>.

<u>Electric heaters</u> are the <u>exception</u> to this. They're <u>100% efficient</u> because <u>all</u> the electricity is converted to "<u>useful</u>" heat. What else could it become? Ultimately, <u>all</u> energy <u>ends up as heat energy</u>.

Some important Examples of Efficiency to Learn

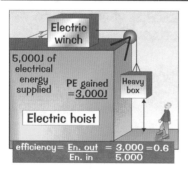

Electric winch
5,000J of electrical energy supplied
PE gained = 3,000J
Heavy box
Electric hoist
efficiency = En. out / En. in = 3,000 / 5,000 = 0.6

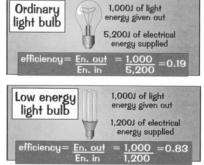

Ordinary light bulb
1,000J of light energy given out
5,200J of electrical energy supplied
efficiency = En. out / En. in = 1,000 / 5,200 = 0.19

Low energy light bulb
1,000J of light energy given out
1,200J of electrical energy supplied
efficiency = En. out / En. in = 1,000 / 1,200 = 0.83

Electric kettle
180,000J of electrical energy supplied
9,000J of heat given out to the room
Think about it!
efficiency = En. out / En. in = 171,000 / 180,000 = 0.95

Learn about energy dissipation — but keep your cool...

The thing about loss of energy is it's always the same — it always disappears as heat and sound, and even the sound ends up as heat pretty quickly. So when they ask "Why is the input energy more than the output energy?", the answer is always the same... <u>Learn and enjoy</u>.

Heat Transfer and Conduction

There are <u>three</u> distinct methods of heat transfer: <u>conduction</u>, <u>convection</u> *and* <u>radiation</u>.
To answer Exam questions, you <u>must</u> use those <u>three key words</u> in just the <u>right places</u>.

Heat Energy Causes Molecules to Move Faster

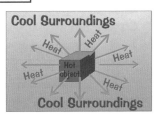

Cool Surroundings
Cool Surroundings

1) <u>Heat energy</u> causes <u>gas and liquid</u> molecules to move around <u>faster</u>, and causes particles in solids to <u>vibrate more rapidly</u>.
2) When particles move <u>faster</u> it shows up as a <u>rise in temperature</u>.
3) This extra <u>kinetic energy</u> in the particles gets <u>dissipated</u> to the <u>surroundings</u>.
4) In other words, the <u>heat energy</u> tends to <u>flow away</u> from a hotter object to its <u>cooler surroundings</u>. But then you knew that already. I would hope.

> If there's a difference in temperature between two places then *HEAT WILL FLOW* between them.

Conduction of Heat — Occurs Mainly in Solids

H O T   **HEAT FLOW**   C O L D

> *CONDUCTION OF HEAT* is the process where *VIBRATING PARTICLES* pass on their *EXTRA KINETIC ENERGY* to *NEIGHBOURING PARTICLES*.

This process continues <u>throughout the solid</u> and gradually the <u>extra kinetic energy</u> (or <u>heat</u>) is passed all the way through the solid, causing a <u>rise in temperature</u> at the other side.

All Metals are Good Conductors due to their Free Electrons

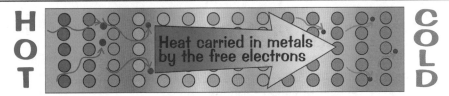

H O T   Heat carried in metals by the free electrons   C O L D

1) Metals "<u>conduct</u>" so well because the electrons are <u>free to move</u> inside the metal.
2) At the <u>hot end</u>, the electrons move <u>faster</u> and <u>diffuse more quickly</u> through the metal.
3) So the electrons <u>carry their energy</u> quite a <u>long way</u> before <u>giving it up</u> in a <u>collision</u>.
4) This is obviously a much <u>faster way</u> of <u>transferring the energy</u> through the metal than slowly passing it between <u>jostling neighbouring atoms</u>. This is why <u>heat travels so fast</u> through <u>metals</u>.

Metals always FEEL hotter or colder because they conduct so well

If a <u>spade</u> is left out in the <u>sunshine</u> the <u>metal</u> part will always <u>feel</u> much <u>hotter</u> than the <u>wooden</u> handle. <u>But it isn't hotter</u> — it just <u>conducts</u> the heat <u>into your hand</u> much quicker than the wood, so your hand <u>heats up</u> much quicker. In <u>cold weather</u>, the <u>metal bits</u> of a spade, or anything else, always <u>feel colder</u> because they <u>take the heat away</u> from your hand quicker. But they're <u>not colder</u>... Remember that.

Good conductors are always metals? — what about Henry Wood...

Phew, no more numbers and formulas, now we're back to good old straightforward factual learning again. Much less confusing — but no less of a challenge, it has to be said. You've really got to make a fair old effort to get this stuff about heat transfer all sorted out in your head so that you know exactly what's going on and when it occurs. <u>Learn and grin</u>.

Convection and Radiation

Convection and radiation are the other two forms of heat transfer — make sure you know all this.

Convection of Heat — Liquids and Gases Only

<u>Gases and liquids</u> are usually free to <u>slosh about</u> — and that allows them to transfer heat by <u>convection</u>, which is a <u>much more effective process</u> than conduction.
Convection simply <u>can't happen in solids</u> because the particles <u>can't move</u>.

> Convection occurs when the more energetic particles <u>move</u> from the <u>hotter region</u> to the <u>cooler region</u> — <u>and take their heat energy with them</u>.

When the <u>more energetic</u> (i.e. <u>hotter</u>) particles get somewhere <u>cooler</u> they then <u>transfer their energy</u> by the usual process of <u>collisions</u> which warm up the surroundings.

Heat Radiation can Travel through a Vacuum

<u>Heat radiation</u> is <u>different</u> from the <u>other two methods</u> of heat transfer in quite a few ways:

1) Heat radiation (or <u>infrared radiation</u>) travels in <u>straight lines</u> at the <u>speed of light</u>.
2) It travels through a <u>vacuum</u>. This is the <u>only way</u> that heat can reach us from the <u>Sun</u>.
3) It can be very effectively <u>reflected away again</u> by a <u>silver surface</u>.
4) It only travels through <u>transparent media</u>, like <u>air</u>, <u>glass</u> and <u>water</u>.
5) Its behaviour is <u>strongly dependent</u> on <u>surface colour and texture</u>.
6) <u>No particles</u> are involved. It's transfer of heat energy <u>purely</u> by <u>waves</u>.

Emission and Absorption of Heat Radiation

1) <u>All objects</u> are <u>continually</u> emitting and absorbing <u>heat radiation</u>.
2) The <u>hotter</u> they are, the <u>more</u> heat radiation they <u>emit</u>.
3) <u>Cooler ones</u> around them will <u>absorb</u> this heat radiation. You can <u>feel</u> this <u>heat radiation</u> if you stand near something <u>hot</u> like a fire.

It Depends an Awful Lot on Surface Colour and Texture

1) <u>Dark matt</u> surfaces <u>absorb</u> heat radiation falling on them much more <u>strongly</u> than <u>bright glossy</u> surfaces, such as <u>gloss white</u> or <u>silver</u>. They <u>also emit</u> heat radiation <u>much more</u> too.
2) <u>Silvered</u> surfaces <u>reflect</u> nearly all heat radiation falling on them.
3) In the lab, there are several fairly dull experiments to demonstrate the <u>effects of surface</u> on <u>emission</u> and <u>absorption</u> of <u>heat radiation</u>. Here are two of the most gripping:

Leslie's Cube

The <u>matt black</u> side <u>emits most heat</u> so its that thermometer which gets <u>hottest</u>.

The <u>matt black</u> surface <u>absorbs most heat</u> so its wax <u>melts</u> first and the ball bearing <u>drops</u>.

The Melting Wax Trick

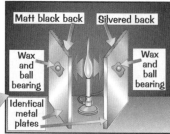

Learn the facts on heat transfer — but don't get a sweat on...

Oi! Watch out! It's another pair of Physics words that look so much alike that half of you think they're the same word. Look: CONVECTION. See, it's different from CONDUCTION. Tricky that one isn't it. Just like reflection and refraction. Not just a different word though — convection is a <u>totally different process</u> too. Make sure you learn exactly <u>why</u> it isn't like conduction.

Heat Transfer and Insulation

Conduction, Convection and Radiation Compared

These differences are really important — make sure you learn them:

1) <u>Conduction</u> occurs mainly in <u>solids</u>.
2) <u>Convection</u> occurs mainly in <u>gases and liquids</u>.
3) Gases and liquids are <u>very poor conductors</u> — convection is usually the <u>dominant process</u>. Where convection <u>can't</u> occur, the heat transfer by <u>conduction</u> is <u>very slow indeed</u> as the diagram of the immersion heater shows. This is a classic example, so <u>learn it</u>.
4) <u>Radiation</u> travels through anything <u>see-through</u>, including a <u>vacuum</u>.
5) <u>Heat radiation</u> is given out by <u>anything</u> which is <u>warm or hot</u>.
6) The <u>amount</u> of heat radiation which is <u>absorbed or emitted</u> depends on the <u>colour</u> and <u>texture</u> of the <u>surface</u>. But don't forget, <u>convection and conduction</u> are totally <u>unaffected</u> by surface colour or texture. A <u>shiny white</u> surface <u>conducts</u> just as well as a <u>matt black</u> one.

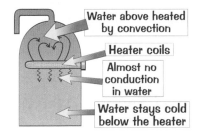

Water above heated by convection
Heater coils
Almost no conduction in water
Water stays cold below the heater

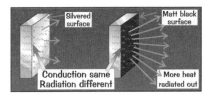

Silvered surface — Matt black surface
Conduction same Radiation different — More heat radiated out

Good Conductors and Good Insulators

1) All <u>metals</u> are good <u>conductors</u> e.g. iron, brass, aluminium, copper, gold, silver etc.
2) All <u>non-metals</u> are good <u>insulators</u> (except <u>graphite</u>).
3) Gases and liquids are truly <u>abysmal conductors</u> (but are great <u>convectors</u> don't forget).
4) The <u>best insulators</u> are ones which <u>trap pockets of air</u>. If the air <u>can't move</u>, it <u>can't</u> transfer heat by <u>convection</u> and so the heat has to <u>conduct</u> very slowly through the <u>pockets of air</u>, as well as the material in between. This really slows it down <u>bigstyle</u>.
This is how <u>clothes</u> and <u>blankets</u> and <u>loft insulation</u> and <u>cavity wall insulation</u> and <u>polystyrene cups</u> and <u>pretty woollen mittens</u> and <u>little furry animals</u> and <u>fluffy yellow ducklings</u> work.

Insulation should also take account of Heat Radiation

1) <u>Silvered finishes</u> are highly effective <u>insulation</u> against heat transfer by <u>radiation</u>.
2) This can either keep heat radiation <u>out</u> or keep heat <u>in</u>.
3) <u>Matt black</u> is rarely used for its thermal properties of <u>absorbing</u> and <u>emitting</u> heat radiation.
4) It's only <u>useful</u> where you want to <u>get rid of heat</u>, e.g. the <u>cooling fins</u> or <u>radiator</u> on an engine.

KEEPING HEAT RADIATION OUT:
Spacesuits
Cooking foil on the turkey
Thermos flasks

KEEPING HEAT IN:
Shiny metal kettles
Survival blankets
Thermos flasks (again)

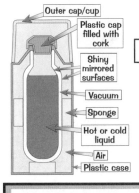

Outer cap/cup
Plastic cap filled with cork
Shiny mirrored surfaces
Vacuum
Sponge
Hot or cold liquid
Air
Plastic case

The Thermos Flask

1) The glass bottle is <u>double-walled</u> with a <u>thin vacuum</u> between the two walls. This stops <u>all conduction and convection</u> through the <u>sides</u>.
2) The walls either side of the vacuum are <u>silvered</u> to keep heat loss by <u>radiation</u> to a <u>minimum</u>.
3) The bottle is supported using <u>insulating foam</u>, minimising <u>conduction</u>.
4) The <u>stopper</u> is made of <u>plastic</u> and filled with <u>cork or foam</u> to reduce <u>conduction</u>.

Heat Transfer and Insulation — keep taking it all in...

There's a lot more to insulation than you first realise. That's because there are <u>three ways</u> that heat can be transferred, and so effective heat insulation has to deal with <u>all three</u>, of course. The venerable Thermos Flask is the classic example of all-in-one full-blown insulation. <u>Learn it</u>.

Keeping Buildings Warm

Loft Insulation
Initial Cost: £200
Annual Saving: £50
Payback time: 4 years

Hot Water Tank Jacket
Initial Cost: £10
Annual Saving: £15
Payback time: 1 year

Thermostatic Controls
Initial Cost: £100
Annual Saving: £20
Payback time: 5 years

Double Glazing
Initial Cost: £3,000
Annual Saving: £60
Payback time: 50 years

Cavity Wall Insulation
Initial Cost: £500
Annual Saving: £70
Payback time: 7 years

Draught-proofing
Initial Cost: £50
Annual Saving: £50
Payback time: 1 year

Effectiveness and Cost-effectiveness are not the same...

1) The figures above are all in the right ballpark, but of course it'll vary from house to house.

2) The cheaper methods of insulation tend to be a lot more cost-effective than the pricier ones.

3) The ones that save the most money each year could be considered the most "effective", e.g. the cavity wall insulation above. How cost-effective it is depends on what timescale you're looking at.

4) If you subtract the annual saving from the initial cost repeatedly then eventually the one with the biggest annual saving must always come out as the winner, if you think about it.

5) But you might sell the house (or die) before that happens. If instead you look at it over, say, a five-year period then the cheap and cheerful draught-proofing wins. Who's to say?

6) But double glazing is always by far the least cost-effective, which is kinda comical, considering.

Know Which Types of Heat Transfer are Involved:

1) CAVITY WALL INSULATION — foam squirted into the gap between the bricks reduces convection and radiation across the gap.

2) LOFT INSULATION — a thick layer of fibreglass wool laid out across the whole loft floor reduces conduction and radiation into the roof space from the ceiling.

3) DRAUGHT PROOFING — strips of foam and plastic around doors and windows stop draughts of cold air blowing in, i.e. they reduce heat loss due to convection.

4) DOUBLE GLAZING — two layers of glass with an air gap reduce conduction and radiation.

5) THERMOSTATIC RADIATOR VALVES — these simply prevent the house being over-warmed.

6) HOT WATER TANK JACKET — lagging such as fibreglass wool reduces conduction and radiation from the hot water tank.

7) THICK CURTAINS — big bits of cloth you pull across the window to stop people looking in at you, but also to reduce heat loss by conduction and radiation.

They don't seem to have these problems in Spain...

Remember, the most effective insulation measure is the one which keeps the most heat in, (biggest annual saving). If your house had no roof, then a roof would be the most effective measure, would it not... But cost-effectiveness depends very much on the timescale involved.

Energy Resources

There are <u>twelve</u> different types of <u>energy resource</u>.
They fit into <u>two broad types</u>: <u>renewable</u> and <u>non-renewable</u>.

Non-renewable Energy Resources will Run Out One Day

The <u>non-renewables</u> are the <u>three FOSSIL FUELS</u> and <u>NUCLEAR</u>:

1) <u>Coal</u>

2) <u>Oil</u>

3) <u>Natural gas</u>

4) <u>Nuclear fuels</u> (<u>uranium</u> and <u>plutonium</u>)

a) They will <u>all run out</u> one day.
b) They all do <u>damage</u> to the environment.
c) But they provide <u>most of our energy</u>.

Renewable Energy Resources will Never Run Out

The <u>renewables</u> are:

1) <u>Wind</u>

2) <u>Waves</u>

3) <u>Tides</u>

4) <u>Hydroelectric</u>

5) <u>Solar</u>

6) <u>Geothermal</u>

7) <u>Food</u>

8) <u>Biomass (wood)</u>

a) These will <u>never run out</u>.
b) They <u>are much less harmful to the environment</u> (except visually).
c) The trouble is they <u>don't provide much energy</u> and some of them are <u>unreliable</u> because they depend on the <u>weather</u>.

The Sun is the Ultimate Source for Nine of the Energy Resources

(The exceptions are tides, nuclear and geothermal — see below)
You need to know the <u>energy transfer chains</u> for all *nine* of them starting from the <u>Sun</u>.
There are however only *five* basic <u>energy chains</u>:

1) <u>Sun</u> ➡ <u>light energy</u> ➡ <u>plants</u> ➡ <u>photosynthesis</u> ➡ *BIOMASS* (wood) or *FOOD*.

2) <u>Sun</u> ➡ <u>light energy</u> ➡ <u>photosynthesis</u> ➡ <u>dead plants/animals</u> ➡ *FOSSIL FUELS*.

3) <u>Sun</u> ➡ <u>heats atmosphere</u> ➡ <u>creates *WINDS*</u> ➡ <u>and therefore *WAVES* too</u>.

4) <u>Sun</u> ➡ <u>heating sea water</u> ➡ <u>clouds</u> ➡ <u>rain</u> ➡ *HYDROELECTRICITY*.

5) <u>Sun</u> ➡ <u>light energy</u> ➡ *SOLAR POWER*.

The Sun Generates Its Energy by Nuclear Fusion Reactions

1) <u>Hydrogen nuclei</u> fuse together to form <u>helium nuclei</u>.
2) This <u>energy</u> is eventually given off as <u>EM waves</u> which reach the Earth as <u>light and heat radiation</u>.

Nuclear, Geothermal and Tidal Energy Do NOT Originate in the Sun

1) <u>Nuclear power</u> comes from the energy <u>locked up</u> in the <u>nuclei of atoms</u>.
2) <u>Nuclear decay</u> also creates heat <u>inside the Earth</u> for <u>geothermal energy</u>, though this happens <u>much slower</u> than in a nuclear reactor.
3) <u>Tides</u> are caused by the <u>gravitational attraction</u> of the <u>Moon</u> and <u>Sun</u>.

Stop fuelling around and learn this stuff properly...

There's a lot of details here on sources of energy — an awful lot of details. Trouble is, in the Exam they could test you on any of them, so I guess you just gotta learn 'em. Most of this page seems to be made up of lists, which is quite a novelty. There you go then, life isn't all bad.

Section Nine — Forces, Energy and Radioactivity

Power Stations Using Non-Renewables

Most of the electricity we use is generated from the four NON-RENEWABLE sources of energy (coal, oil, gas and nuclear) in big power stations, which are all pretty much the same apart from the boiler. Learn the basic features of the typical power station shown here and also the nuclear reactor.

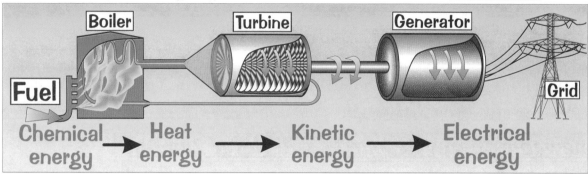

Boiler — Turbine — Generator — Fuel — Grid

Chemical energy → Heat energy → Kinetic energy → Electrical energy

Nuclear Reactors are Just Fancy Boilers

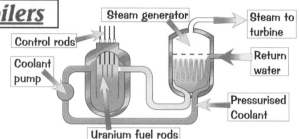

Steam generator — Steam to turbine — Control rods — Coolant pump — Return water — Pressurised Coolant — Uranium fuel rods

1) A nuclear power station is mostly the same as the one shown above, where heat is produced in a boiler to make steam to drive turbines etc. The difference is in the boiler, as shown here:
2) They take the longest time of all the non-renewables to start up. Natural gas takes the shortest time.

Environmental Problems with the use of Non-Renewables

1) All three fossil fuels, (coal, oil and gas) release CO_2. For the same amount of energy produced, coal releases the most CO_2, followed by oil then gas. All this CO_2 adds to the Greenhouse Effect, causing global warming. There's no feasible way to stop it being released either. Ho hum.
2) Burning coal and oil releases sulphur dioxide which causes acid rain.
This is reduced by taking the sulphur out before it's burned or cleaning up the emissions.
3) Coal mining makes a mess of the landscape, especially "open-cast mining".
4) Oil spillages cause serious environmental problems. We try to avoid it, but it'll always happen.
5) Nuclear power is relatively clean but the nuclear waste is very dangerous and difficult to dispose of.
6) Nuclear fuel (i.e. uranium) is cheap but the overall cost of nuclear power is high due to the costs of the power plant, final decommissioning and the storage of waste.
7) Nuclear power always carries the risk of a major catastrophe like the Chernobyl disaster.

The Non-Renewables Need to be Conserved

1) When the fossil fuels eventually run out we will have to use other forms of energy.
2) More importantly however, fossil fuels are also a very useful source of chemicals, (especially crude oil) which will be hard to replace when they are all gone.
3) To stop the fossil fuels running out so quickly there are two things we can do:

1) Use Less Energy by Being More Efficient with it:

(i) Better insulation of buildings,
(ii) Turning lights and other things off when not needed,
(iii) Making everyone drive spiddly little cars with puny little engines.

2) Use More of the Renewable Sources of Energy

as detailed on the following pages.

Learn about the non-renewables — before it's too late...

Make sure you realise that we generate most of our electricity from the four non-renewables, and that the power stations are all pretty much the same, as exemplified by the above diagram. Also make sure you know all the problems about them and why we should use less of them.

Wind Power and Hydroelectric Power

Wind Power — Lots of Little Wind Turbines

1) This involves putting <u>lots of windmills</u> (wind turbines) up in <u>exposed places</u> like on <u>moors</u> or round <u>coasts</u>.

2) Each wind turbine has its own <u>generator</u> inside it so the electricity is generated <u>directly</u> from the <u>wind</u> turning the <u>blades</u>, which <u>turn the generator</u>.

3) There's <u>no pollution</u>.

4) But they do <u>spoil the view</u>. You need about <u>5000 wind turbines</u> to replace <u>one coal-fired power station</u> and 5000 of them cover <u>a lot</u> of ground — that wouldn't look very nice at all.

5) There's also the problem of <u>no power when the wind stops</u>, and it's <u>impossible</u> to <u>increase supply</u> when there's <u>extra demand</u>.

6) The <u>initial costs are quite high</u>, but there are <u>no fuel costs</u> and <u>minimal running costs</u>.

Hydroelectricity and Pumped Storage Systems

1) <u>Hydroelectric power</u> usually requires the <u>flooding</u> of a <u>valley</u> by building a <u>big dam</u>.

2) <u>Rainwater</u> is caught and allowed out <u>through turbines</u>. There is <u>no pollution</u>.

3) There is quite a <u>big impact</u> on the <u>environment</u> due to the flooding of the valley and possible <u>loss of habitat</u> for some species. The reservoirs can also look very <u>unsightly</u> when they <u>dry up</u>. Location in <u>remote valleys</u> (often in <u>Scotland</u> and <u>Wales</u>) reduces some of these problems.

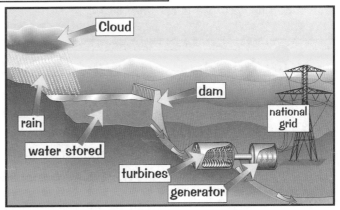

4) A <u>big advantage</u> is <u>immediate response</u> to increased demand and there's no problem with <u>reliability</u> except in times of <u>drought</u> — but remember this is the UK we're talking about.

5) <u>Initial costs are high</u>, but there's <u>no fuel</u> and <u>minimal running costs</u>.

Pumped Storage Gives Extra Supply Just When it's Needed

1) Most large power stations have <u>huge boilers</u> which have to be kept running <u>all night</u> even though demand is <u>very low</u>. This means there's a <u>surplus</u> of electricity at night.

2) It's surprisingly <u>difficult</u> to find a way of <u>storing</u> this spare energy for <u>later use</u>.

3) <u>Pumped storage</u> is one of the <u>best solutions</u> to the problem.

4) In pumped storage, 'spare' <u>night-time electricity</u> is used to pump water up to a <u>higher reservoir</u>.

5) This can then be <u>released quickly</u> during periods of <u>peak demand</u> such as at <u>tea time</u> each evening, to supplement the <u>steady delivery</u> from the big power stations.

6) Remember, <u>pumped storage</u> uses the same <u>idea</u> as Hydroelectric Power but it <u>isn't</u> a way of <u>generating</u> power — but simply a way of <u>storing energy</u> which has <u>already</u> been generated.

Learn about Wind Power — it can blow your mind...

Lots of important details here on these nice green squeaky clean sources of energy — pity they make such a mess of the landscape. Three nice green squeaky clean <u>mini-essays</u> please.

Wave Power and Tidal Power

Don't confuse <u>wave power</u> with <u>tidal power</u>. They are <u>completely different</u>.

Wave Power — Lots of little Wave Converters

1) You need lots of small <u>wave generators</u> located <u>around the coast</u>.

2) As waves come in to the shore they provide an <u>up and down motion</u> which can be used to drive a <u>generator</u>.

3) There is <u>no pollution</u>. The main problems are <u>spoiling the view</u> and being a <u>hazard to boats</u>.

4) They are <u>fairly unreliable</u>, since waves tend to die out when the <u>wind drops</u>.

5) <u>Initial costs are high</u> but there's <u>no fuel</u> and <u>minimal running costs</u>. Wave power is never likely to provide energy on a <u>large scale</u>, but it can be <u>very useful</u> on <u>small islands</u>.

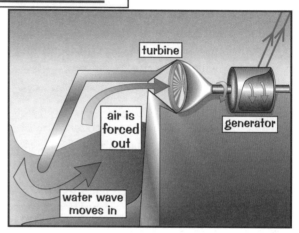

Tidal Barrages — Using the Sun and Moon's Gravity

1) <u>Tidal barrages</u> are <u>big dams</u> built across <u>river estuaries</u> with <u>turbines</u> in them.

2) As the <u>tide comes in</u> it fills up the estuary to a height of <u>several metres</u>. This water can then be allowed out <u>through turbines</u> at a controlled speed. It also drives the turbines on the way in.

3) There is <u>no pollution</u>. The source of the energy is the gravity of the Sun and the Moon.

4) The main problems are <u>preventing free access by boats</u>, <u>spoiling the view</u> and <u>altering the habitat</u> of the wildlife, e.g. wading birds, sea creatures and beasties who live in the sand.

5) Tides are <u>pretty reliable</u> in the sense that they happen <u>twice a day without fail</u>, and always near to the <u>predicted height</u>. The only drawback is that the <u>height</u> of the tide is <u>variable</u> so lower (neap) tides will provide <u>significantly less energy</u> than the bigger "<u>spring</u>" tides. But tidal barrages are <u>excellent</u> for <u>storing energy</u> ready for periods of <u>peak demand</u>.

6) <u>Initial costs are moderately high</u> but there's <u>no fuel</u> and <u>minimal running costs</u>. Even though it can only be used in a <u>few</u> of the <u>most suitable estuaries</u> tidal power has the potential for generating a <u>significant amount</u> of energy.

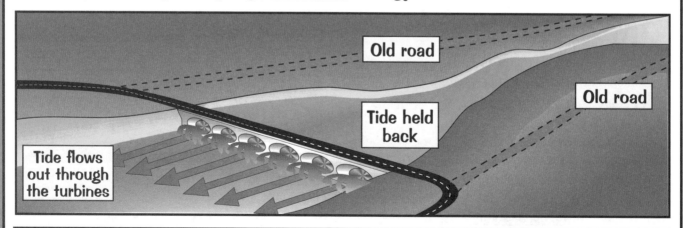

Learn about Wave Power — and bid your cares goodbye...

I do hope you appreciate the big big differences between tidal power and wave power. They both involve salty sea water, sure — but there the similarities end. Lots of jolly details then, just waiting to be absorbed into your cavernous intra-cranial void. Smile and enjoy. And <u>learn</u>.

Section Nine — Forces, Energy and Radioactivity

Geothermal and Wood Burning

Geothermal Energy — Heat from Underground

1) This is <u>only possible</u> in <u>certain places</u> where <u>hot rocks</u> lie quite near to the <u>surface</u>. The source of much of the heat is the <u>slow decay</u> of various <u>radioactive elements</u> including <u>uranium</u> deep inside the Earth.

2) <u>Water is pumped</u> in pipes down to <u>hot rocks</u> and <u>returns as steam</u> to drive a <u>generator</u>.

3) This is actually <u>brilliant free energy</u> with no real environmental problems.

4) The <u>main drawback</u> is the <u>cost of drilling</u> down <u>several km</u> to the hot rocks.

5) Unfortunately there are <u>very few places</u> where this seems to be an <u>economic option</u> (for now).

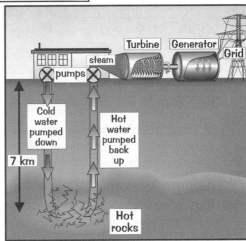

Wood Burning — Environmentally OK

1) This can be done <u>commercially</u> on a <u>large scale</u>.

2) It involves the cultivation of <u>fast-growing trees</u> which are then <u>harvested</u>, <u>chopped up</u> and <u>burned</u> in a power station <u>furnace</u> to produce <u>electricity</u>.

3) Unlike <u>fossil fuels</u>, wood burning does <u>not</u> cause a problem with the <u>Greenhouse Effect</u> because any CO_2 released in the burning of the wood was <u>removed</u> when they <u>grew in the first place</u>, and because the trees are grown <u>as quickly as they are burnt</u> they will <u>never run out</u>. This does <u>NOT apply</u> to the burning of <u>rainforests</u> where the trees take <u>much longer</u> to grow.

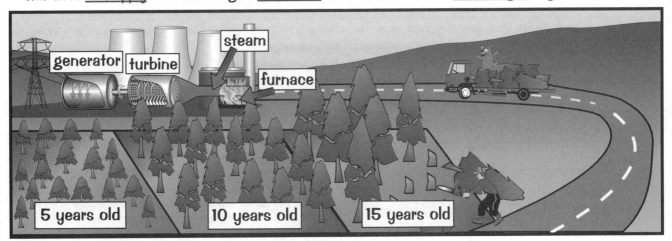

4) The <u>main drawback</u> is the <u>use of land</u> for <u>growing trees</u>, but if these woods can be made into <u>recreational areas</u> then that may be a <u>positive benefit</u> and certainly the woodlands should look quite <u>attractive</u>, as opposed to 5000 wind turbines covering miles and miles of countryside.

5) As a method of electricity generation, wood burning may seem mighty <u>old-fashioned</u>, but if enough trees are grown this is a <u>reliable and plentiful source of energy</u>, with fewer environmental drawbacks than many other energy resources.

6) Initial costs <u>aren't too high</u>, but there's some cost in <u>harvesting and processing</u> the wood.

Wood Burning to solve the energy crisis? — barking mad...

I reckon on geothermal energy as being the big source of power for the next millennium or two. All you have to do is drill down 10 or 20 km and you're sorted — limitless free energy. Anyway, two more squeaky clean <u>mini-essays</u> just crying out to be <u>scribbled</u>. Enjoy.

<u>Solar Energy and Comparison</u>

<u>Solar Energy</u> — <u>Solar Cells, Solar Panels</u> and <u>Solar Furnaces</u>

<u>LEARN</u> the <u>three different ways</u> that solar energy can be harnessed:

1) <u>SOLAR CELLS</u> generate <u>electric currents directly</u> from sunlight. They are <u>expensive initially</u>. Solar cells are the best source of energy for <u>calculators</u> and <u>watches</u> which don't use much electricity. <u>Some remote places</u> (including satellites) don't have a choice — they have to use solar power.

2) <u>SOLAR PANELS</u> are much less sophisticated. They simply contain <u>water pipes</u> under a <u>black surface</u>. <u>Heat radiation</u> from the Sun is <u>absorbed</u> by the <u>black surface</u> to <u>heat the water</u> in the pipes.

3) A <u>SOLAR FURNACE</u> is a large array of <u>curved mirrors</u> which are all <u>focused</u> onto one spot to produce <u>very high temperatures</u> so water can be turned to <u>steam</u> to drive a <u>turbine</u>.

In all cases there is <u>no pollution</u>. In sunny countries solar power is a <u>very reliable source</u> of energy — but only in the <u>daytime</u>. Solar power will still provide <u>some energy</u> even in <u>cloudy countries</u> like Britain. <u>Initial costs</u> are <u>high</u> but after that the energy is <u>free</u> and <u>running costs almost nil</u> (apart from the <u>solar furnaces</u> which are more complicated).

<u>Comparison of Renewables and Non-Renewables</u>

1) They're quite likely to give you an Exam question asking you to "<u>evaluate</u>" or "<u>discuss</u>" the <u>relative merits</u> of generating power by <u>renewable</u> and <u>non-renewable</u> resources.

2) The way to <u>get the marks</u> is to simply write down the <u>pros and cons</u> of each method.

3) Full details are given on the last few pages. However there are some <u>clear generalisations</u> you should <u>definitely learn</u> to help you answer such questions. Make sure you can <u>list these easily from memory</u>:

<u>Non-Renewable Resources (Coal, Oil, Gas and Nuclear):</u>

<u>ADVANTAGES:</u>

1) Very <u>high</u> output.
2) <u>Reliable</u> output, entirely <u>independent of the weather</u>.
3) Don't take up much <u>land</u> or spoil too much <u>landscape</u>.

<u>DISADVANTAGES:</u>

1) Very <u>polluting</u>.
2) <u>Mining or drilling</u>, then <u>transportation</u> of fuels damages the environment.
3) They're <u>running out</u> quickly.

<u>Renewable Resources (Wind, Waves, Solar, etc.):</u>

<u>ADVANTAGES:</u>

1) <u>No pollution</u>.
2) They will <u>never run out</u>.
3) <u>Don't damage the environment</u> (except visually).
4) <u>No fuel costs</u>, although the initial costs are high.

<u>DISADVANTAGES:</u>

1) Require <u>large areas of land</u> or water.
2) They don't always deliver <u>when needed</u> — if the weather isn't right, for example.
3) <u>Don't provide much energy</u>.

<u>Solar Cells are like Fried Eggs — always best sunny side up...</u>

Watch out for it — there are <u>three</u> different ways of using solar power directly. <u>Learn</u> all three. And make sure you learn <u>all</u> that summary comparing renewables and non-renewables. Phew.

Atoms and Radioactivity

Energy's stored in the nuclei of atoms too — that's where nuclear power comes from. And that's where radioactivity comes from as well. Now, people used to think that atoms were tiny solid balls. But it turned out that atoms were actually made up of even smaller particles. Oooh, fancy that...

Rutherford's Scattering and the Demise of the Plum Pudding

1) In 1804 John Dalton said matter was made up of tiny solid spheres which he called atoms.

2) Later they discovered electrons could be removed from atoms. They then saw atoms as spheres of positive charge with tiny negative electrons stuck in it like plums in a plum pudding.

3) Then Ernest Rutherford and his merry men tried firing alpha particles at a thin gold foil. Most of them just went straight through, but the odd one came straight back at them, which was frankly a bit of a shocker for Ernie and his pals.
Being pretty clued up guys though, they realised this meant that most of the mass of the atom was concentrated at the centre in a tiny nucleus, with a positive charge.
This means that most of an atom is just made up of empty space, which is also a bit of a shocker when you think about it.

Radioactivity comes from Unstable Nuclei

Unstable nuclei will decay and in the process give out radiation. This process is entirely random. This means that if you have 1000 unstable nuclei, you can't say when any one of them is going to decay, and neither can you do anything at all to make a decay happen.
Each nucleus will just decay quite spontaneously in its own good time. It's completely unaffected by physical conditions like temperature or by any sort of chemical bonding etc.

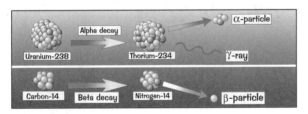

When the nucleus does decay it will spit out one or more of the three types of radiation, alpha, beta or gamma, and in the process the nucleus will often change into a new element.

Background Radiation comes from Many Sources

1) Natural background radiation comes from:

i) Radioactivity of naturally occurring unstable isotopes which are all around us — in the air, in food, in building materials and in the rocks under our feet.

ii) Radiation from space, which is known as cosmic rays. These come mostly from the Sun.

iii) Radiation due to human activity, e.g. fallout from nuclear explosions or dumped nuclear waste. But this represents a tiny proportion of the total background radiation.

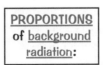

PROPORTIONS of background radiation:

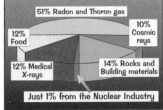

2) At high altitudes (e.g. in jet planes) it increases because of more exposure to cosmic rays.

3) Underground in mines, etc. it increases because of the rocks all around.

4) Certain underground rocks can cause higher levels at the surface, especially if they release radioactive radon gas, which tends to get trapped inside people's houses. This varies widely across the UK depending on the rock type, as shown:

Background Radiation — it's no good burying your head in the sand...

Yip, it's funny old stuff is radiation, that's for sure. It is quite mysterious, I guess, but just like anything else, the more you learn about it, the less of a mystery it becomes.

The Three Types of Radiation

There are three different types of radiation — and you need to know about them all.

Nuclear Radiation: Alpha, Beta and Gamma (α, β and γ)

You need to remember a couple of things about each type of radiation:
1) What they actually are.
2) How strongly ionising they are (i.e. how good they are at bashing into atoms and knock electrons off).
There's a pattern: The further the radiation can penetrate before hitting an atom and getting stopped, the less damage it will do along the way and so the less ionising it is.

Alpha Particles are Helium Nuclei $_2^4\text{He}$

1) Alpha particles consist of two protons and two neutrons.
   They are relatively big and heavy and slow moving.
2) They therefore don't penetrate into materials but are stopped quickly by things like paper and skin.
3) Because of their size they are strongly ionising, which just means they bash into a lot of atoms and knock electrons off them before they slow down, which creates lots of ions — hence the term "ionising".

Beta Particles are Electrons $_{-1}^{0}\text{e}$

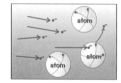

1) These are in between alpha and gamma in terms of their properties.
2) They move quite fast and they are quite small (they're electrons).
3) They penetrate moderately before colliding (but are stopped by a thin sheet of aluminium, for exaample) and are moderately ionising too.
4) For every β–particle emitted, a neutron turns to a proton in the nucleus.

Gamma Rays are Very Short Wavelength EM Waves

1) They are the opposite of alpha particles in a way.
2) They penetrate a long way into materials without being stopped, although a thick sheet of lead or concrete can stop them).
3) This means they are weakly ionising because they tend to pass through rather than colliding with atoms. Eventually they hit something and do damage.

The Radioactivity of a Sample Always Decreases Over Time

1) This is pretty obvious when you think about it. Each time a decay happens and an alpha, beta or gamma is given out, it means one more radioactive nucleus has disappeared.
2) Obviously, as the unstable nuclei all steadily disappear, the activity as a whole will also decrease. So the older a sample becomes, the less radiation it will emit.
3) How quickly the activity drops off varies a lot. For some it takes just a few hours before nearly all the unstable nuclei have decayed, whilst others last for millions of years.
4) The problem with trying to measure this is that the activity never reaches zero, which is why we have to use the idea of half-life to measure how quickly the activity drops off.
5) Learn this important definition of half-life:
   Another definition of half-life is:
   "The time taken for the activity (or count rate) to fall by half". Use either.

> HALF-LIFE is the TIME TAKEN for HALF of the radioactive atoms now present to DECAY

Learn the three types of radiation — it's easy as abc...

Alpha, beta and gamma. You do realise those are just the first three letters of the Greek alphabet don't you: α, β, γ — just like a, b, c. They might sound like complex names to you but they were just easy labels at the time. Anyway, learn all the facts about them — and scribble.

Uses of Radioactive Materials

Below are the <u>main uses</u> for radioactive isotopes. Make sure you <u>learn</u> why each application uses a <u>particular radioisotope</u> according to its <u>half-life</u> and the <u>type of radiation</u> it gives out.

1) Radiotherapy — the Treatment of Cancer Using γ-Rays

1) Since high doses of gamma rays will <u>kill all living cells</u>, they can be used to <u>treat cancers</u>.
2) The gamma rays have to be <u>directed carefully</u> and at just the right <u>dosage</u> so as to kill the <u>cancer cells</u> without damaging too many <u>normal cells</u>.
3) However, a <u>fair bit of damage</u> is <u>inevitably</u> done to <u>normal cells</u> which makes the patient feel <u>very ill</u>. But if the cancer is <u>successfully killed off</u> in the end, then it's worth it.

2) Sterilisation of Food and Surgical Instruments Using γ-Rays

1) A <u>high dose</u> of <u>gamma rays</u> will <u>kill</u> all <u>microbes</u> in food and keep it <u>fresh for longer</u>.
2) <u>Medical instruments</u> can be <u>sterilised</u> in the same way, rather than by boiling them.
3) The great <u>advantage</u> of <u>irradiation</u> over boiling is that it doesn't involve <u>high temperatures</u>, so things like <u>fresh apples</u> or <u>plastic instruments</u> can be totally <u>sterilised</u> without <u>heat damage</u>.
4) The food is <u>not</u> radioactive afterwards, so it's <u>perfectly safe</u> to eat (though there are concerns about chemical changes and nutrient loss).
5) The isotope used for this needs to be a <u>very strong</u> emitter of <u>gamma rays</u> with a <u>reasonably long half-life</u> (at least several months) so that it doesn't need <u>replacing</u> too often.

3) Smoke detectors

1) A <u>weak</u> radioactive source is placed in the detector, close to <u>two electrodes</u>.
2) The source causes <u>ionisation</u>, and a <u>current</u> flows as a result.
3) If there's a fire then smoke will <u>absorb</u> the radiation — the current stops and the <u>alarm sounds</u>.

4) Thickness Control in Industry and Manufacturing

1) You have a <u>radioactive source</u> and you direct it <u>through the stuff being made</u>, usually a continuous sheet of <u>paper</u> or <u>cardboard</u> or <u>metal</u> etc.
2) The <u>detector</u> is on the <u>other side</u> and is connected to a <u>control unit</u>.
3) When the amount of radiation detected <u>goes down</u>, it means the stuff is coming out <u>too thick</u> and so the control unit <u>pinches the rollers up</u> a bit to make it <u>thinner</u> again.
4) If the reading <u>goes up</u>, it means it's <u>too thin</u>, so the control unit <u>opens the rollers out</u> a bit. It's all clever stuff, but the most <u>important thing</u>, as usual, is the <u>choice of isotope</u>.
5) Firstly, it must have a <u>long half-life</u> (several <u>years</u> at least), otherwise the strength would <u>gradually decline</u> and the control unit would keep <u>pinching up the rollers</u> trying to <u>compensate</u>.
6) Secondly, the source must be a <u>beta source</u> for <u>paper and cardboard</u>, or a <u>gamma source</u> for <u>metal sheets</u>. This is because the stuff being made must <u>partly</u> block the radiation. If it <u>all</u> goes through (or <u>none</u> of it does) then the reading <u>won't change</u> at all as the thickness changes. Alpha particles are no use for this since they would <u>all be stopped</u>.

Will any of that be in your Exam? — isotope so...

Radioactive isotopes are also used in the medical world and industry as <u>tracers</u>. In medicine, a <u>radioactive isotope</u> is <u>injected</u> into a patient — and its progress about the body can be <u>detected</u>. It's then easy to see if (and where) it's being <u>absorbed</u> (or not being absorbed). In much the same way, you can find a <u>leaky pipe</u> by squirting in a radioactive isotope and detecting where it's <u>leaking out</u>.

Detection Of Radiation

The Geiger-Müller Tube and Counter

1) This is the most familiar type of radiation detector. You see them on TV documentaries going click-click-clickety-click, whilst the grim-faced reporter delivers a sombre message of impending doom and the terrible state of the planet.

2) This is also the type used for experiments in the lab, as the counter allows you to record the number of counts per minute.

3) When alpha, beta or gamma radiation enters the G-M tube, it ionises the gas inside and triggers an electrical discharge (a spark) which makes a clicking sound and also sends a small signal to the electronic counter. It's so simple even I could have thought of it... but born too late. Sigh.

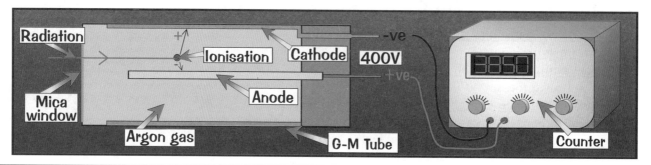

Background Count must always be Subtracted...

See page 119

If you want to find the count rate from a specific source, you must always measure the background count first, (i.e. take the reading with no source present) and then subtract that value from each reading taken using the source. This is especially important if you are plotting the values on a graph to find the half-life.

Radioactivity is Measured in Becquerels, Bq

The unit used for measuring radioactivity is the Becquerel (Bq). One Becquerel is one nucleus decaying per second. So a count rate of 60 counts per minute (60 CPM) would represent 1 Bq.

In fact it's a bit tricky to measure exactly how strong a radioactive source is because the reading you get on your G-M tube/counter depends very much on how close you are to the source and how big the front window is on your G-M tube. A reading in Becquerels really only gives you a sort of vague relative measure of how much radioactivity there is around. A bigger G-M tube or moving closer to the source would give a much bigger reading in counts per second (Bq). Anyway, as long as you know that one Becquerel means one nucleus decaying per second (on average), then you'll be OK in the Exam.

Photographic Film Also Detects Radiation

1) Radiation was first discovered by accident when Henri Becquerel left some uranium on some photographic plates which became "fogged" by it.

2) These days photographic film is a useful way of detecting radiation.

3) Workers in the nuclear industry or those using X-ray equipment such as dentists and radiographers wear little badges which have a bit of photographic film in them.

4) The film is checked every now and then to see if it's got fogged too quickly, which would mean the person was getting too much exposure to radiation.

B91432
17/10/97

You can't see, hear, smell or taste it — just like truth...

Make sure you remember those two ways of measuring radiation: G-M tube and photographic film, and remember what a Becquerel is. This page is ideal for the good old mini-essay method I reckon, just to make sure you've taken all the important points on board. Learn and scribble.

Radiation Hazards and Safety

Radiation Harms Living Cells

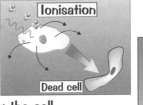

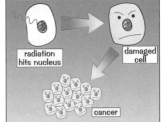

1) <u>Alpha</u>, <u>beta</u> and <u>gamma</u> radiation will cheerfully <u>enter living cells</u> and <u>collide with molecules</u>.
2) These collisions cause <u>ionisation</u>, which <u>damages or destroys</u> the <u>molecules</u>.
3) <u>Lower doses</u> tend to cause <u>minor damage</u> without <u>killing</u> the cell.
4) This can give rise to <u>mutant cells</u> which <u>divide uncontrollably</u>. This is <u>cancer</u>.
5) <u>Higher doses</u> tend to <u>kill cells completely</u>, which causes <u>radiation sickness</u> if a lot of body cells <u>all get blatted at once</u>.
6) The <u>extent</u> of the harmful effects depends on <u>two things</u>:
    a) <u>How much exposure</u> you have to the radiation.
    b) The <u>energy and penetration</u> of the radiation emitted, since <u>some types</u> are <u>more hazardous</u> than others, of course.

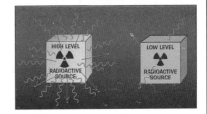

Outside the Body, β- and γ- Sources are the <u>Most Dangerous</u>

This is because <u>beta and gamma</u> can get <u>inside</u> to the delicate <u>organs</u>, whereas alpha is much less dangerous because it <u>can't penetrate the skin</u>.

Inside the Body, an α- Source is the <u>Most Dangerous</u>

<u>Inside the body</u> alpha sources do all their damage in a <u>very localised area</u>. Beta and gamma sources on the other hand are <u>less dangerous</u> inside the body because they mostly <u>pass straight out</u> without doing much damage.

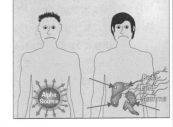

α, β and γ are Ionising Radiation

Ionisation is when an atom either <u>loses</u> or <u>gains</u> one or more <u>electrons</u>. Simple as that — just don't forget it.

You Need to Learn about these Safety Precautions

If you don't <u>already know</u> that radioactive materials need to be handled <u>carefully</u>, then you've probably been asleep for a few years. In the Exam they might ask you to <u>list some specific precautions</u> that should be taken when <u>handling radioactive materials</u>. If you want those <u>easy marks</u> you'd better learn all these:

In the School Laboratory:

1) <u>Never</u> allow <u>skin contact</u> with a source. Always handle with <u>tongs</u>.
2) Keep the source at <u>arm's length</u> to keep it <u>as far</u> from the body <u>as possible</u>.
3) Keep the source <u>pointing away</u> from the body and <u>avoid looking directly at it</u>.
4) <u>Always</u> keep the source in a <u>lead box</u> and put it back in <u>as soon</u> as the experiment is <u>over</u>.

Extra Precautions for Industrial Nuclear Workers:

1) Wearing <u>full protective suits</u> to prevent <u>tiny radioactive particles</u> from being <u>inhaled</u> or lodging <u>on the skin</u> or <u>under fingernails</u> etc.
2) Use of <u>lead-lined suits</u> and <u>lead/concrete barriers</u> and <u>thick lead screens</u> to prevent exposure to γ-rays from highly contaminated areas. (α and β are stopped <u>much more easily</u>.)
3) Use of <u>remote-controlled robot arms</u> in highly radioactive areas.

Radiation Sickness — well yes, it does all get a bit tedious...

Quite a few picky details here. It's easy to kid yourself that you don't really need to know all this stuff. Well take it from me, you <u>do</u> need to know it all and there's only one sure-fire way to find out whether you do or not. Three <u>mini-essays</u> please, with all the picky details in. Enjoy.

Revision Summary for Section Nine

One thing's for sure — there are loads of easy facts to learn in this section. Of course there are still some bits which need thinking about, but really, most of it is fairly easy stuff which just needs learning. Don't forget, this book contains all the important information they've specifically mentioned in the syllabus, and this is precisely the stuff they're going to test you on in the Exams. You must practise these questions over and over again until they're easy.

1) What's the difference between speed and velocity? Give an example of each.
2) What's acceleration? Is it the same thing as speed or velocity? What are the units of it?
3) Sketch a typical distance-time graph and point out all the important parts of it.
4) Sketch a typical velocity-time graph and point out all the important parts of it.
5) Explain how to calculate velocity from a distance-time graph.
6) Explain how to find speed, distance and acceleration from a velocity-time graph.
7) Write down the First Law of Motion. Illustrate with a diagram.
8) If an object has zero resultant force on it, can it be moving? Can it be accelerating?
9) Write down the Second Law of Motion. Illustrate with a diagram. What's the formula for it?
10) Explain the difference between mass and weight. What units are they measured in?
11) What's the formula for weight? Illustrate it with a worked example of your own.
12) What is "terminal velocity"? Is it the same thing as maximum speed?
13) What are the two main factors affecting the terminal velocity of a falling object?
14) List the ten types of energy, and give twelve examples of energy transfers.
15) Write down the Principle of the Conservation of Energy. When is energy actually <u>useful</u>?
16) Sketch the basic energy flow diagram for a typical "useful device".
17) What's the formula for efficiency? What are the three numerical forms suitable for efficiency?
18) What causes heat to flow from one place to another? What do molecules do as they heat up?
19) Give a strict definition of conduction of heat and say which materials are good conductors.
20) Give a strict definition of convection.
21) List five properties of heat radiation. Which kind of objects emit and absorb heat radiation?
22) Which surfaces absorb heat radiation best? Which surfaces emit it best?
23) Explain briefly the difference between conduction, convection and radiation.
24) Draw a fully labelled diagram of a Thermos Flask, and explain exactly what each bit is for.
25) List seven ways of insulating houses and say which are the most <u>effective</u> and which are the most <u>cost-effective</u> measures. How do you decide on cost-effectiveness?
26) List four non-renewable sources of energy and say why they are non-renewable.
27) List eight kinds of renewable energy.
28) Which three energy resources do <u>not</u> originate in the Sun?
29) Which kind of resource do we get most of our energy from? Sketch a typical power station.
30) List seven environmental hazards with non-renewables and four ways that we can use less.
31) Give full details of how we can use wind power, including the advantages and disadvantages.
32) Give full details of how a hydroelectric scheme works. What's pumped storage all about?
33) Sketch a wave generator and explain the pros and cons of this as a source of energy.
34) Explain how tidal power can be harnessed. What are the pros and cons of this idea?
35) Explain where geothermal energy comes from. Describe how we can make use of it.
36) Explain the principles of wood burning for generating electricity. Give the pros and cons.
37) What are the disadvantages of solar power?
38) Describe Rutherford's Scattering Experiment with a diagram, and say what happened.
39) Will anything cause a nucleus to undergo radioactive decay?
40) Describe in detail the nature and properties of the three types of radiation: α, β, and γ.
41) Describe in detail how radioactive isotopes are used in each of the following:
    a) tracers in industry b) sterilisation c) thickness control
    d) treating cancer e) generating power.
42) Draw a labelled diagram of a Geiger-Müller tube and explain what it's for and how it works.
43) How is photographic film used in little badges to monitor radiation?
44) Exactly what kind of damage does radiation do inside body cells?
45) Which kind of sources are most dangerous a) inside the body b) outside the body?
46) List four safety precautions for the school lab, and three more for nuclear workers.

Index

Index